ALMOST GOLDEN

by

John and Robert Mariani

ISBN 978-0-7414-3017-5

Published by:

INFINITY
PUBLISHING.COM

Info@buybooksontheweb.com
www.buybooksontheweb.com
Toll-free (877) BUY BOOK
Local Phone (610) 941-9999
Fax (610) 941-9959

Printed in the United States of America

Published November 2012

Table of Contents

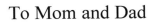

To Mom and Dad

PROLOGUE

My brother John and I were born in the North Bronx neighborhood known as Country Club Road. I am five years older than John and although we grew up together, we lived relatively separate childhoods because of our age difference. We each had or own set of friends. Our own favorite places in the neighborhood to play. And our own experiences.

We moved away from The Neighborhood north to Westchester County in the summer of my sixteenth birthday. John was eleven. At that point, neither of us had ever driven a car. Smoked a cigarette. Made love to a girl. Or gone to anything but Catholic schools. But because we continued to live fairly separate lives under the same roof, we never thought of ourselves as having a lot in common. He was a scholar. I was a barely competent student. I loved to ride horses. He liked to build model airplanes. He liked Gene Autry. I liked The Lone Ranger. After college, I moved to New England, and John stayed in the New York area.

It was not until we were both adults and starting to raise our own families that we noticed how many similar intense childhood memories we actually shared. When we'd get together on holidays, we'd reminisce and it became clear that our kids-- he had two boys, I had two girls—were fascinated with our stories about growing up in the Bronx. It became a kind of ritual to drive them through our old Country Club Road neighborhood and show them the rickety pier where we used to swim; the field where we played baseball and football and ring-a-leaveo; the hills where we used to ride our sleds in winter, and the stores where our mother used to buy mozzarella and prosciutto and fresh Italian bread. We introduced them to chocolate egg creams at Garber's candy store and pizza at Amerigo's restaurant. And we told them stories about our heroic uncles who were sailors and marines in the War; and our beautiful aunts who cooked liked magicians, knew all about opera, and even became "airline hostesses" on some of the earlier transcontinental passenger flights.

One rainy Saturday John and I and our kids were driving past our old 4-family apartment house on Campbell Drive. We stopped to take some snapshots and a woman in her mid-thirties came out and asked what we were doing. When we told her that we used to live there, she asked us if we'd like to come in and see the place. We agreed instantly, feeling as if we were actually going to re-live those years in our life when every smell, every sound, every color had an intensity that could almost set you reeling. I think nostalgia is a very over-used but underrated emotion. It's a way of living in two or three time periods at one time. It's a way of getting back parts of your life you thought had disappeared forever. I guess you could say it's a way of living twice.

The layout of the old apartment had not changed a bit, and even some details like the metal light sconces on the living room wall were still there and functioning. What was different was the size, the scale of everything. It seemed so much smaller. The distance between our bedroom and the living room that used to seem to take forever to navigate when I walked it on Christmas morning as a 7-year old kid, heading for the presents—that distance now was really only about three or four steps.

I looked out our old bedroom window at the backyard which had seemed to me as a child like a vast woodland with a huge tunnel of forsythia you could get lost in, and saw a cramped little plot of land barely big enough for a few tomato plants and a clothesline.

From the living room window you could still glimpse a section of Pelham Bay, its choppy waters the same leaden gray I remembered them being on cloudy days like this one when I was a kid. Standing in the narrow little kitchen, I remembered the smell of my mother sautéing garlic for her red sauce. And the time we came back from a day of fishing with our uncles out on Long Island Sound with a bushel basket of fresh porgies and flounders, which we promptly dumped into the green kitchen sink. As I recall, mom distilled them into an out-of-this-world seafood marinara sauce on angel hair pasta.

John and I thanked the lady for letting us see the old place and left, stepping down off the concrete stoop that had, in our childhood been the deck of a pirate ship, a boxing ring, a Civil War fort, a spaceship, and the setting for an all-night VJ-Day party I shall never forget, although I was only five at the time.

Shortly after this experience, John and I discovered that we had both been writing down our memories of this magical neighborhood. And what was striking was how many times we both had chosen to write about the same experiences. Blizzards. Movie theaters. Neighborhood heroes. And the rats that finally invaded our apartment, driven there by a hurricane that had rushed up the mouth of the Bay one sultry September.

The idea for this book arose out of all this—these memories set down by two brothers who have discovered that they have a great deal more in common than they'd ever realized as kids

WHERE ARE WE?

By Rob Mariani

"Wait a minute. I thought you said we were going to the Bronx."

"This *is* the Bronx. Country Club Road, the Bronx."

"No. *This* is the *Bronx*?"

"The Bronx. Yeah. My old neighborhood."

"This can't be the Bronx. Where's the projects? Where's the street gangs? The traffic and the abandoned cars? This has *trees* for Godsake."

"I told you, this is a part of the Bronx you never see. It's a little secret, this area."

"You grew up here."

"Yeah. Here's our old house. 3305 Campbell Drive. From our living room window you could just see a glimpse of Pelham Bay between those other two houses. And that big old house across the street there, the Providence Rest rest home. It used to be a private house owned by these two little old ladies named Davis. Sisters. One was deaf and she talked like a baby. The other one talked like a witch. They'd let us

1

play in the woods all around their house. We used to play guns, ring-a-leaveo, sword fighting. Go sledding down their hill in the winter. There's a seawall in the back we used to go fishing off of."

"This is like the Riviera. In the Bronx!"

"This was just a workingman's neighborhood back then. When I lived here everybody's father was either a fireman or a pipe fitter, or maybe they owned a bar or a hardware store up on Burhe Avenue."

"What kind of name is that? 'Burhe?'"

"I don't know, Dutch, I think.

"My father, he was a chiropodist in Westchester Square. The house right next to the Davis's there? That one on the right with the Bay right in the back yard—Doctor Perotta used to live there. He had this inboard speedboat. And these two big Great Danes. And three gorgeous daughters.

"And there, that's Mr. Yule's house. He was an air raid warden. During the War he went around with his flashlight and his helmet making sure everybody had their lights out and their shades down. In case the Nazis tried to bomb us.

"Right along here near the bus stop? That was my grandmother's house. They just tore it down and replaced it with that white brick monstrosity.

"This block here, Polo Place, there used to be a big open field here. I doubt if anyone ever played polo on it. 'Woof-Woof Field,' we called it. I think because somebody once said that all the dogs used to take a crap there. But it was really pretty clean. We played baseball and football here. Made our own baseball diamonds. Flattened out tin cans for bases. Now it's all these houses. But these are about the only new houses they've built since I was here as a kid. Every place else is pretty much the same as I left it back in 1956. No house over two stories high. Every one with a little backyard. And from practically every house, if you can't see

2

the Bay, you can always smell it. Especially when the tide's going out."

"What's that place with the adobe roof?"

"That's the Spanish nun's convent. Used to be a vacant lot where we played all the time. We called it 'The Roslyn.' Then Richie Swift burned it down and they built the convent. Richie was my best friend from the time I was like 7. I lost track of him a long time ago though."

"This a school here next to the convent?"

"The Villa Maria Academy. It's an all girls' school except when I was a kid they took boys in first and second grades only. I went there my first two years of school. It's run by nuns—Mother Saint Arthur. Mother Saint Patronella. They could be tough"

"I still can't believe this is the Bronx. There's trees and grass and birds and it's so... so quiet."

"Well, like I told you, this little neighborhood was—and still is-- like a little bit of heaven. It's like that until you cross Bruckner."

"Bruckner?"

"Bruckner Boulevard. Another Dutch name. You cross over that, go past the Indian museum a little ways and then the *other* Bronx starts—the one everybody always thinks of when you say 'the Bronx'."

THE NEIGHBORHOOD.

By John Mariani

Where we lived was called Country Club, a name that may sound strange to people who imagine the Bronx as an unrelieved territory of burned-out buildings, abandoned cars, wailing police sirens and drug shoot-outs. But back in the '50s all that was just beginning, and most of the Bronx was still a pretty nice place to live.

There were some sections that were changing and some tough places where you didn't go without your friends. Kingsbridge was going bad. We heard about gang fights in Bedford Park. And Castle Hill had seen better days.

But most neighborhoods were still solid ethnic enclaves. The Italians lived around Fordham, the Irish in Mott Haven, and the Puerto Ricans were moving in around Crotona Park. The working-class Jews lived in Hunts Point, the middle-class Jews moved up to the Grand Concourse and the rich Jews began to occupy the great Riverdale mansions along the Hudson that had been built by some of New York's most patrician families.

It really wasn't until after the Civil War that the Bronx attracted development, but when the Third Avenue subway reached 169th Street in 1888, the land was opened up to the immigrant families who regarded it as a rural alternative to the cramped, claustrophobic tenements of Little Italy, the Lower East Side, Harlem and Hell's Kitchen. For them the Bronx was the countryside, a vast stretch of green land and farms that extended from Manhattan to Westchester County, wholly separated from the other New York City boroughs, bound to the south by the murky Harlem River, on the west by the majestic, fast-flowing Hudson, and on the east by the shifting waters of the Long Island Sound.

The neighborhoods those families moved into all had the names of much earlier immigrants, the Indians, the Dutch and the English, although the Bronx itself was named after a seventeenth-century Danish Lutheran named Jonas Bronck, who paid two kettles, two guns, two adzes, two cows, one barrel of cider, six pieces of silver and two shirts for 500 acres between the Harlem River and another river that took his name. It was quite a bit more than Peter Minuit paid for the island of Manhattan.

In 1642 a free-thinking Boston dissenter named Anne Hutchinson and her family settled in the area, only to be wiped out by Indians within the year. By 1664 the British had seized control of the Bronx, which had grown to 42 square miles of territory. Despite the English dominance, many of the old Dutch names survived in streets and sections like Van Cortlandt Park, De Reimer Avenue, Vreeland Avenue and Spuyten Duyvil. Even a few of the older Indian names have lasted the centuries, like Mosholu Avenue, which meant "smooth stones" of a kind found in the nearby brook. But for the most part the new settlers went about Anglicizing the Bronx as much as possible with names like Grosvenor, Fordham, Pelham, Tremont and Kingsbridge.

The section where we lived had been developed out of the rambling Van Antwerp estate, which during the American Revolution had been Ferris farm, and before that the vast Underhill family holdings. By the time we lived there in the

1940s the streets had acquired marvelously eccentric and honorific names. To go by the street signs you'd think we were the cradle of American Arts & Industry: A local philanthropist Isaac L. Rice, president of an electric storage battery company, imparted a progressive theme to the neighborhood by naming streets Radio and Research as well as after inventors George Ohm, John Watt, Andre Ampere, and Thomas Edison, while Eugene Rosenquist, president of the Westchester Electric Light Company, indulged his passion for Wagnerian opera by giving streets Teutonic names like Lohengrin, Parsifal, Valhalla and Siegfried.

By the time we got there the neighborhood was solidly middle class, though a few well-off doctors still lived rather splendidly in the big houses along the water, always built of stone to keep out the storms that swept in off the Sound each fall and winter. But for the most part ours was a neighborhood of second- and third-generation families with Italian, Irish, Scandinavian, German and Polish roots.

There really was a country club at Country Club, and it was located down at the end of our street, Campbell Drive, which was named after a forgotten Protestant vestryman who apparently married well. By the 1940s it was no longer much of a country club, but it had once been something quite grand, spread over 25 acres, and very exclusive, with a yachtsmen's marina, a golf course and a beautifully landscaped polo field.

By the 1940s, though, the Club had lost all ties to that kind of affluence. However grand it had once been, it had become decrepit and was falling apart. What was left was a clubhouse and a few dank locker rooms set on a sea wall, from which a wooden pier jutted out into the Long Island Sound. Every time we went there it looked like another strut had rotted away or fallen off the barnacle-encrusted pilings that held it up.

That's where most of the teenagers hung out, showing off by diving off the pier into the shallow, rocky green-gray

6

waters of the Sound or smoking cigarettes and flicking them into the water when an adult came near. The little kids played on a tiny stretch of sand below the seawall. No one could bring themselves to call this ten yards of sand a "beach," and it was always strewn with thousands of mussel, clam and scary-looking, hairy horseshoe crab shells and ugly ribbons of translucent green seaweed. Then, too, the occasional "Coney Island whitefish" would float ashore, otherwise known as a used condom.

From the pier you could look northward up to Westchester County--the suburbs, where a lot of people in the Bronx were already thinking of moving--and south to the gracefully arched, pale blue Whitestone Bridge, which had been built to link New York City to the 1939 World's Fair. Beyond the bridge stood the spires of Manhattan, a concrete city that bore no resemblance to our neighborhood, which was green and lined with trees, open lots, houses and garden apartments.

The tight, interlocking grid pattern of streets in Manhattan, Brooklyn, Queens and much of the South and West Bronx had never been imposed upon the north Bronx, which up until the 1930s had been largely rural, even pastoral. A branch of the elevated Third Avenue subway terminated at Pelham Bay Park, and when you got off there, you came down the loud iron steps of the station and found yourself looking eastward to fields and woodlands where mothers took their children in strollers and where seagulls swooped in off the water and down to pick at the scraps of food left behind. The park had two golf courses, riding trails, even a lagoon for shell racing.

The north Bronx had been built along serpentine lines that conformed on one side to the eddies and juttings of the Sound and to the wide, palisades-bound Hudson on the other. Streets curved in the Bronx and avenues were very broad, with room for trolley cars that were still running well after the Second World War. The aptly named Grand Concourse was built as a conduit for Manhattanites to reach the Bronx parklands and was originally designed with separate pathways for carriages, pedestrians and automobiles.

The first parkways in America were in the Bronx and were so called because they were designed to encourage people to take a drive, pull over to the side of the well-landscaped road, and have a picnic. Unlike the ugly post-war Thruways built to link major American cities, the parkways were built not to be the shortest or straightest distance between two points but to be the most beautifully adapted to the natural landscape. This had been the original ideal of Frederick Law Olmstead, who had designed Central Park in Manhattan and who sought to tether the great urban parks of New York by a network of tree-lined parkways. More than thirty years passed before a semblance of Olmstead's vision was pressed into pavement, but ultimately only in the Bronx were all the parks--Van Courtlandt, Pelham Bay, Bedford, Crotona, Claremont, the Botanical Gardens and the Bronx Zoo--actually connected to one another.

The first was the Bronx River Parkway, completed in 1925, and the Hutchinson River (also built to rush people to the World's Fair), the Mosholu, and the Pelham Bay Parkways all followed within a few years.

The smaller streets of the North and East Bronx wound in and out of the neighborhoods, so that you'd find yourself coming back to where you started after meandering past open fields, rows of garden apartments, schools and small stores. Or you might be driving along down a small, straight street and, without any warning at all, stop dead in front of a seawall with nowhere to go but backwards.

If people asked you where you lived, you'd first mention the section of the Bronx, then maybe the subway stop, or a local church, then an identifying landmark, like a guy's sister.

"So where you from?"

"Up near Throgs Neck."

"Whereabouts?"

"You know the Pelham Bay station?"

"Yeah."

"Just down from there. You know Annunciation?"

"The big church on Middletown Road? Sure."

"O.K., Country Club's just across Bruckner Boulevard. That's where I live. On Campbell Drive."

"O.K., right. I know a guy who lives up there named Richie Swift. You know Richie Swift?"

"Richie? Hey, he lives like three houses away. He's like my best friend in the world."

"Yeah, Richie's a good guy. He's got a sister, right? With big tits?"

"Big is not the word. They are like headlights!

"Right. O.K. I know exactly where you live. Jeez, that's a real nice section of the Bronx. Real nice."

WAR BABY.

By Rob Mariani

When the Japanese attacked Pearl Harbor on December 7th, 1941, I was just one year old, the first child of two Italian-Americans, Eligio and Renee Mariani. Within the next 48 hours after the Pearl Harbor bombing, Italy joined Japan and Germany in declaring war on the United States. I, of course, have no memory of that period, but it was an uneasy, paranoid time for a generation of people like my parents. People with an Italian heritage.

Having both been born here in this country, all my parents knew of Italy was what their parents had told them. My mother's mother, Alvina, and her husband, Charlie Sofia, were both born here in America as well, and they adored their country. Alvina was brought up in Harlem at a time when there were still goats and chickens running loose in front yards, where many streets were still un-paved, and where there were no such things as subways or race riots. She taught her four daughters to love the U.S. of A., constantly reminding them that they were not "Italians," and they were not even "Italian-Americans."

"You're just Americans," she'd say, looking up at her daughters from a bowl of soft white dough that her fingers were transforming into little puff-lets of gnocchi. "You were born *here*, not in Italy. That's 'the Old Country, Italy."

Very few members of my parents' ilk sided with Mussolini and his fascist regime. Any who showed the slightest empathy with Il Duce were quickly shunned. Most Italian Americans either hastened to join the U.S. military or were drafted and went overseas to fight against the lantern-jawed dictator and his evil cohorts. Still, there were stories in the news about Italian-Americans being herded into "camps" out in California. Everybody was pretty damn nervous.

Just about all of my uncles went into some branch of the service. There was Uncle Phil on my mother's side, who joined the army and ended up in the Cavalry. (We had a black and white photo of him riding an Army mule); and his brother, Uncle Paul, who became a paratrooper in the Army Air Corp. My Aunt Corrine's husband, "Red" Cronin, signed up with the Marines soon after the War began and he fought in some of the Pacific Theater's bloodiest battles.

Then there were the friends of our family whom we *called* "Uncle." "Uncle" Walter Hopkins, was a young lawyer/jokester with a Don Amiche mustache and a bombastic voice that seemed specifically designed to deliver punch lines. He was from Yonkers and became a Navy lieutenant in the AG's office in Okinawa. (The only war story that I ever heard him tell was about the time he had to share a latrine with a little old Okinawan lady. He was embarrassed; the lady was totally nonplused.)

Our "Uncle" Bill Verlin, who had the office adjacent to my father's, joined the Army Air Corps to use his skills as a dentist. He served his stint peacefully in Florida where his wife, May, and their new baby, "Little Bill," joined him. My impression was that "Uncle" Bill actually made more money as an Army dentist than he did as a civilian at that time. But he was a quiet man of few words who became even quieter, the more highballs he consumed.

Then there was "Uncle" Willy who was the very opposite of quiet. He survived The Battle of the Bulge and remained in the Army all his life, eventually reaching the rank of Lieutenant General. "Uncle" Willy was a wild man who shouted when he talked. He drove a dark green Ford coupe with a rumble seat that folded open in the back. His wife, who weighed about 92 pounds soaking wet, was named "Honey." "Uncle" Willy would do almost anything to get a rise out of us as kids, including putting lit cigarettes out on his tongue, and throwing firecrackers up into the air and catching them with his bare hand as they exploded.

At one point during the middle of the War, the only man in my parents' group of friends who wasn't wearing a uniform was my father, Eligio. I've never had a full explanation of why this was so. It was not due to any lack of patriotism on his part. At that time, he was struggling to start his career as a chiropodist in the Bronx's Westchester Square and was hard put just to make the rent on our little two-bedroom apartment on Campbell Drive. My mother was still recuperating from a difficult pregnancy that concluded with my caesarian delivery. Apparently, unlike his friends who were all assured of officer status because of their professional backgrounds, dad would have had to become a buck private in the Army had he enlisted. This meant very low pay, of course, and the very real possibility of being sent into combat in some armed capacity.

I was told years later that dad had received some kind of temporary draft deferment because he was the sole supporter of a family; but towards the end of the War, he lost the deferment and was re-classified 1A. When it seemed like he was going to be drafted into the Army, he tried to enlist in the Navy with the hope of gaining officer status as a chiropodist. But there were no such slots available in any of the services for men of that profession. They told him that some professionals had to stay behind to cater to Americans. Fortunately, the end of the War came just in time and he was spared.

I know on the one hand that dad was relieved for his family's sake. But on the other hand, I think he always felt a bit ashamed that he hadn't served his country in its time of need. Especially since his name, like Beneto Mussolini's, ended in a vowel. To compensate, and dispel any hint that he might be somehow sympathetic to his ancestral roots, dad became a real American flag-waver. It was not a pose. His love for America was as strong and genuine as anyone's and he was always the first to denounce the wrong turn that Italy had taken under the Fascists. Nevertheless, he still loved the Italian culture—the opera, Ezio Pinza, and Michelangelo, and he was proud of the rapid advances my mother was making in learning to cook traditional Italian food-- along with her all-American repertoire of Virginia hams and Sunday afternoon meat loafs.

My actual memories of World War II, although I lived through all of it, are vague and impressionistic at best. There's a very vivid image of a jubilant "Uncle" Willy on VJ Day jitterbugging with his wife Honey around our front stoop on Campbell Drive as fireflies flecked the night sky. A darker memory of him recalls Christmas Eve shortly after the War had ended. He was remembering a midnight mass that he thought would be his last in a frozen little German town surrounded by Nazi forces. At the end of the tale, he flung his highball glass into the fireplace and collapsed crying into his wife's lap.

During the War, I can recall the voices of the radio newscasters coming over our cream-colored Bakelite Emerson kitchen radio with the sounds of bombs and fighter planes behind them, and the Pathe' Newsreels that showed our troops charging off landing barges onto a beach exploding with enemy fire.

There were the pink and yellow food rationing coupon books my mother had to take to the butcher shop and the grocery store where she'd exchange them for a rather meager piece of chuck steak or a few overripe artichokes.

There was the crazy, finger-jabbing Andrews Sisters all singing with one voice about "The Boogie Woogie Bugle Boy of Company 'C' " that made war seem like real fun and a great way to meet girls.

And I remember with strange fascination a Sunday afternoon when my Uncle Phil, home from the War and, newly settled into his neat little Levittown house with his lovely wife Ann, showed my dad and me his collection of military trophies. They were items he had liberated from the hated Nazis—swords with flying eagles on their hilts, lethal looking bayonets, and swastika armbands that without using any words, seemed to say "Stand up and Salute me!"

Another part of the War I can remember vaguely, was the pride and joy both my parents took in the success of their backyard Victory Garden, as if the big healthy beefsteak tomatoes and the bright orange carrots they'd grown were somehow proof that they were indeed serving their country "behind the lines."

WHERE WE CAME FROM.

By John Mariani

Between 1880 and 1920 one out of every four immi-grants who came to America was from Sicily, the gorgeous but impoverished volcanic island at the toe of Italy where they'd lived close to subsistence on land barely freed from feudalism.

Never remote from invasion, Sicily had once been a great center of Hellenic culture, envied by Imperial Rome, one of a series of foreign invaders who for two millennia subjugated the island. Through countless rebellions against foreign tyrants--always, in the end a lost cause--Sicilians had developed stratagems for survival based on a self-imposed insularity and Byzantine secret societies. They maintained a dialect incomprehensible to other Italians, and when they emigrated to America, they kept to themselves.

Of the five million Italians who came to the United States over that forty-year period, the next largest group, after the Sicilians, were from Campania, the province of Naples, a steaming city of extraordinary opulence and natu-ral beauty beneath which lay the same legacy of poverty, corruption and deprivation that drove the Sicilians out of their country.

"See Naples and die!" was the beloved, operatic motto of the city, whose panorama of Vesuvius and the Bay of Naples and whose richness of churches, catacombs, antiquities, gardens and markets astonished foreign visitors, as did the widespread squalor, disease and stench with which its populace lived.

Naples was always a city of two faces. Oscar Wilde, who visited in 1900, called it "evil and luxurious." Mark Twain, who was there in the 1860s, found the sight of the city "a picture of wonderful beauty. . . a vast mosaic of many colors; the lofty islands swimming in a dreamy haze in the distance." But he also cautioned his readers "do not go within the walls and look at it in detail," describing the people as "filthy in their habits, and this makes filthy streets and breeds disagreeable sights and smells." Twain went so far as to make a vicious joke about Neapolitans' susceptibility to cholera, saying, "before the doctor can dig through the dirt and get at the disease the man dies."

These, along with throngs of other Southern Italians from Abruzzi, Apulia, Basilicata, Calabria and Molise, came to America believing it was a land of milk and honey--two commodities in short supply among Italian immigrants. They believed the stories of freedom from hunger, disease and grinding, unrelenting poverty. They knew nothing of voting, of democracy or of political power, but they would have to learn quickly or be controlled by new, more sophisticated masters.

Many times the head of the family would come over first, work for a year or two, save all his money, then send for his wife and children. Some eventually made enough money to move back to the Old Country where they could afford to buy a piece of the old feudal lands and to live better than their ancestors might ever have dreamed. Others returned because they hated the life and the discrimination they found in America. But most stayed and settled in Italian

16

communities in the eastern cities, particularly New York.

They came over in steerage, and their first sight of America, usually at dawn, was the lighted torch of the Statue of Liberty, like a mother looking for her lost children. A gift of the people—not the government—of France, its size and majesty, the work of an Alsatian sculpture, took on the immediate, embracing iconography of a wonder of the world, and held for the immigrants the same tantalizing seductiveness as a Homeric siren.

If a contagious disease were found onboard, the ship might be quarantined for weeks before people were let off. They'd arrive at Ellis Island, whose Great Hall had been magnificently tiled by Rafaelle y Guastavino, who did the same for the vaults of the 59th Street Bridge and the Grand Central Oyster Bar. There the people would be herded like cattle with hundreds of others into pens, where they'd wait silently and fearfully for hours, then be taken away to be examined for cholera, tuberculosis and other infectious diseases; those who showed any signs of such maladies were turned back. A mere case of pink eye could destroy all their dreams in the seconds it took an American doctor to look at them.

If they passed through they'd be lucky to be met by relatives who had preceded them. Most newcomers, however, were approached by contractors who would sign them up for jobs as house painters, ditch diggers, fruit pickers, garbage collectors and tree choppers. Unless they had a trade, they took what they could get. The good contractors were those who took least advantage of the immigrants, though the Italians were always dreadfully underpaid; the worst stole their money and belongings and left them stranded in shanty work towns a hundred miles from New York.

The Italians spoke no English and the contractors spoke no Italian, so the immigrants were often given New World names on the spot. Their last names, which invariably came from the towns they'd left behind, like Salerno, Costanza,

Ragusa, Catania, Stromboli, Messina and Paterno, were Anglicized or simply concocted by the job foreman.

That's how my great grandfather, Paolo Girolamo, a hod carrier, got the name "Paul Ross," and how the children of my great uncle, Patrizio Girolamo, a plasterer who worked on the Waldorf-Astoria and the Metropolitan Opera House, came to be called "Gillo," because their grammar school teacher could not spell their true name and they could not yet read or write.

Except for a few artisans, furniture makers, tailors, and plasterers, the Sicilians had mainly been *contadini* in the Old Country, farm people who'd never received any formal education at all and whose culture and spirituality was owed exclusively to their childlike faith in a Roman Catholic Church that had for hundreds of years helped maintain the very status quo that perpetuated their poverty and ignorance. It was a mystical, matriarchal Church that offered little but misery and sorrow in this life, promising peace and happiness only when the *contadini* were returned to soil they had worked for centuries but could never hope to own. Meanwhile they were encouraged to have as many children as God would send to build the Army of Christ.

The Northern Italians had long looked upon all Southerners as inferiors and referred to the swarthy, almost Arablooking Sicilians with belligerent disdain, calling them *"africani"* (Africans). So rare were Northern Italians from, say, Tuscany or Piedmont, in America that fair-haired *biondi* (blondes) were remarked upon as if there were a saintly aura around them, and it was automatically assumed they were smarter, richer and more cultivated. This deeply rooted self-abnegation among Southern Italians kept the first generation of Sicilians and Neapolitans huddled together in the tenements of lower Manhattan and Harlem. They spoke in their secretive dialects, so that not even Italians from other provinces could understand what they were saying. Even Jacob Riis, whose spent his life chronicling the immigrant experience, wrote in exasperation of the Italian immigrant, "His ignorance and unconquerable suspicion of strangers dig the pit into which he falls. He not only knows no word of English, but he does not know enough to learn."

Some Italians banded together in defensive gangs, at first to protect their own people and neighborhoods but soon to extort money from those same sources. The Mafia, which had originated as small medieval peasant armies employed by landowners for protection and peace and which Sicilians called by the name *onorata societa*--"honored society"-- began this way in America but soon developed into gangs of extortionists. With the onset of Prohibition, these mobsters' murderous activities, threats of violence and crooked money gained them access into the unions, the government and the police precincts. Meanwhile, like the brigands and strong arms who had for centuries brutalized the Sicilians back in the Old country, they victimized the Italian immigrants in New York in every way possible.

It became clear to those illiterate, dark-complexioned, very shrewd immigrants who had already survived centuries of numbing repression and extortion that in America the way out of poverty was by educating their young. In America education was not just available to them but expected of them, given to them free, and that by sending one's children off each morning to American schools, they would learn English, begin to understand the stratagems used against them, and then master the game. But in the process, they would become more like Americans and less like Sicilians and Neapolitans.

For the most part, then, education was widely encouraged among the Italian children, though probably not so much as in Jewish families, of whom it was said that books were "a means of flight from the restrictions and squalor of the Brooklyns and Bronxes" of the period. It was a source of pride that a son or daughter could read but the children felt shamed by their parents' illiteracy. Most Italian families before World War II were content if their sons got through high school and their daughters through grade school, all the while assimilating into American culture, quickly losing linkage to their Italian heritage.

Within a generation, Italian-Americans had stopped speaking Italian anywhere but at home, and within another generation, it was rare to hear it spoken even there. The younger Italian-Americans never learned it. The older ones never used the little they knew. In its place was a patois with a New York accent, heavily inflected with Italian sounds and expressions. A drawn out "a-a-ay" could begin or end any number of sentences to express anything from delight to disappointment, as in "A-a-ay, that's a beautiful car you got dere" or "A-a-ay, I don't need this crap-ola tonight." A litany of curse words were strewn like red flags throughout sentences for emphasis, though never in the company of women.

Like their parents, they still talked furiously with their hands, their eyes, their shoulders and their hips. Gestures were both dramatic and subtle, ostentatious and discreet. Arms would flail to the heavens in mock horror. The slightest arching of an eyebrow could mean trouble. Biting a lip was the prelude to a brawl. And if a girl slowly averted her eyes from a boy, it was clear to him that she loved him.

They were deeply religious, though the men did not often go to the new churches sprung up in every community. It was enough that the men had built them so exquisitely, with the hardest granite, the best brick, the finest polished marble and stained glass, and the most beautiful woods and mosaic tiles. The stucco workers, painters and stonecutters saw themselves in the image of Michelangelo and Bernini and Brunelleschi. They took massive blocks of white marble from quarries in Tuckahoe, up in Westchester County, and cut them into the cornerstones of churches, as well as into the temples of American democracy like the Washington Monument, the Lincoln Memorial and the Federal Reserve Bank in New York.

Their handiwork, from the small parish churches to the magnificent cathedrals in Manhattan, Brooklyn and the Bronx, were not only testaments to their abiding faith and gratitude to God and their patron saints but were manifest expressions of the immigrants' success in the New World. These were churches built for the greater glory of God, but they were also built to show the nobility of work as performed by the immigrant worker.

If an Italian had a lawn or a backyard on his property, he would invariably put a statue of a fair-haired, blue-eyed Virgin Mary standing in an Italian grotto, her skin as white as cream, her glowing heart exposed, her foot crushing the head of a demon serpent.

Religious art among the Italians was almost always flamboyant, full of martyred saints, beautiful virgins, and infant Jesuses dressed up in extravagantly bejeweled crowns and costumes of red satin and the most delicate lace. Once, when an Infant of Prague's costume caught fire from a votive candle and burned down half of my aunt Cosie's house, she shrugged and said, "Had it not been for the Infant's intercession, the whole house would have burned down."

When the Sicilians and Neapolitans arrived in America, these holy figures were their only heroes and heroines. But within a single generation the Italian-Americans had flesh-and-blood heroes and heroines to inspire and fill them with pride. There was Mother Cabrini, a nun who worked among the poor Italian immigrants and became--miracle of miracle!--the first American saint.

The immigrants delighted in the extraordinary achievements of Italians like Enrico Caruso--a Neapolitan!--who became principal tenor of the Metropolitan opera. And Luisa Tetrazzini, the coloratura soprano who thrilled audiences around the world. Italians named spaghetti dishes after both of them.

But none brought greater glory to the Italians than Fiorello LaGuardia, the "Little Flower." Half-Jewish, half-Italian, LaGuardia was born in a tenement, never finished high school but spoke seven languages, had a style that was part demagogue and part parish priest, and ran--and won--on a ticket that promised an end to the power wielded by the Irish-dominated Tammany bosses that ran New York like a feudal fiefdom.

Italians had learned the importance of political power early on--something over which they'd had no control in Italy-- and they learned to work with the city bosses, get the contracts to build the roads, the schools, the parks and the tunnels.

Some, like my grandfather Charlie Sofia, became part of the process. Born in East Harlem, he moved to the Bronx, ran horse stables, then, with his brothers, started a successful moving van business. But because he was a stalwart member of the Jackson Democratic Club and helped pull in the votes, he found himself appointed secretary to a Bronx judge at an astounding salary of $5,000 a year. He was particularly well known for getting black people in Harlem to register and vote, driving them to the polls in his big convertible car.

By the end of World War I the Italians, Irish and Jews had come to re-settle the old Dutch and English lands called the Bronx, and their new apartments were a far cry from the tenements of Little Italy, the Lower East Side, Hell's Kitchen and Harlem. The apartments were much larger. The streets were wider and cleaner, the density of the buildings lower, the air was better, and within blocks there were green parks, parish churches in profusion, and boulevards broader than those of Rome. The majestic, faux-Gothic Fordham University campus, and, just to the east, the magnificent Botanical Gardens and the Bronx Zoo were municipal treasures that put to shame even the most splendid estates of the aristocrats back in the Italy. And these wonderful places were built for everyone's education and pleasure, from the lowest to the highest classes.

The Italians kept pretty much to themselves. So did the Jews, the Irish and the Germans. But there was always an overlap, and, despite the attempts on the part of the old-timers to maintain the old ways, their sons and daughters of Sicily and Naples and Abruzzo and Basilicata had begun to distance themselves from their heritage quickly and with little regret. They'd forgotten the melodic dialects and were often ashamed of the coarseness of their parents. They were also ashamed of *being* ashamed.

They went to school with children with unpronounceable names like McGillicuddy, Stephanapoulos, Lindquist, Padrewski, and Schwartz. And all the while their parents worried that their daughters would marry such people and lose their own name or their religion, which would put their very souls in danger of perdition.

This was the world in flux into which my mother and father were born.

TWO KINDS OF ITALIANS.

By Rob Mariani

They were separated by only one generation, but that generation was a pivotal one. Eligio Mariani, or "Ellie" as his family called him for short, was a first-generation Italian from the Fordham Road neighborhood, which was heavily Italian, right across from the august bastion of Jesuit authority, Fordham University. Both Eligo's parents, Michelangelo and Rosa, had been born in the little Adriatic Sea-side town of Vasto, Italy. Finding no work there in the 1920's, they'd come to America as a young married couple with their infant daughter, Rose. Their two sons, Louis and Eligio were both born and raised here, in the Bronx.

Neither of my father's parents, Michelangelo nor Rosa Mariani, ever really mastered the English language. Grandpa worked as a machinist and a maker of mechanical toys, and then he manufactured wire and wooden industrial sock dryers in his own little sawdust-covered shop under the elevated subway—the "L"--near Castle Hill Avenue. I guess most of his customers spoke Italian or he had someone translate for him. But everyone in his Fordham Road neighborhood spoke Italian. He could probably go for days without encountering English. As a kid, I never remember him ever addressing me in anything but a very gruff, low-voiced and unintelligible Italian as he affectionately grasped my cheek between his first two calloused fingers. I think he was amused (if not elated) by the fact that I was the first child in the family born with blond-ish hair and blue eyes. I can still see the black lines on his hands and the dark crescent of grime beneath his thumbnail. A workingman's hands.

I don't believe that Grandpa Mariani really resisted learning English; rather he just had very little need to do so. His kids all spoke Italian at the dinner table and English outside the home and in school. Evidently they learned both languages by ear as they grew up in an Italian neighborhood that was slowly becoming Americanized.

Rosa, Grandma Mariani, on the other hand, had a very strong desire to maintain her ties with her Italian origins and language. According to my mother, her mother-in-law made it a point *not* to learn English. I got the impression she never truly embraced America and that perhaps she even had dreams of one day returning to her little hometown of Vasto. She lived out her life here as an alien and died young while I was just an infant. She never met my brother John.

My mother, Renee Sofia, was a very different breed of Italian from the Marianis. She was *second* generation, born in the Pilgrim Avenue section of the North Bronx surrounded by a mixture of new Americans. Even the name of her street resonated with patriotic, early American overtones. Both her parents, Charlie and Alvina Sofia were born and raised in a bucolic Harlem that would be unrecognizable today.

This second generation of Italians had caught a glimpse of "The American Dream" and were hell-bent on achieving it, which meant becoming as American as possible and making their kids full-fledged, Horatio Alger-Andy Hardy-Shirley Temple-style Americans. There was a deliberate attempt on the part of my mother's parents to jettison any-thing that smacked of their Mediterranean heritage. They spoke only English, (except of course when they were cooking or discussing food-- there's no English word for "gnocchi"), and they tried to emulate the American icons of the time—the Clark Gables, the Jimmy Stewarts, the Gary Coopers, the Lucile Balls, the Betty Grables, and Judy Garlands. They listened to American music, learned American History, and were infatuated with stars like Harry James, The Andrew Sisters, and the pianist, Frankie Carl. They coveted a well-kept home in the suburbs, read the writings of Thomas Jefferson and Alexander Hamilton, and flew the American flag proudly on holidays. And during World War II, they made it clear that they had no sympathy whatever for the Fascists who had ruthlessly taken over the Italian government.

My mother, Renee (always pronounced "RAY-nay") Theodora Sofia, was the oldest of the four Sofia girls. Her sisters were Vivian, Corrine (nicknamed "Cosie"), and Marilyn. Renee Sofia met Eligio Mariani when they were in high school although they were from different neighborhoods and slightly different social strata. Grandpa Mariani worked with his hands; Grandpa Sofia worked as a judge's secretary in an office, behind a desk. Both, however, always wore a suit and tie to work every day. It distinguished them from their relatives who dug the subways, the sewers, built the dams and the new skyscrapers of New York.

Somehow Renee and Eligio's paths crossed up around my mother's Pilgrim Avenue neighborhood. As she tells it, Eligio—or "Al" as she quickly chose to re-name him to dispel any "dago" connotations—captured her attention when he showed up one day wearing royal blue knickers with white socks and a jaunty, matching white cap. She was smitten by his debonair style and his irresistible warmth. I think, though, that she wished Al had been from a background that was not quite so immediately Italian.

Al was equally taken with Renee's girlish laugh and animated eyes, even her pronounced buck teeth. And he was

26

infatuated with her peppy, upbeat, all-American bobby-soxer ways. Not only was she someone he could envision spending the rest of his life with, but she was a step closer to being a pure-bred daughter of the America he so wanted to be part of.

Once Al left the Fordham Road neighborhood, his friends became, for the most part, "true Americans," people like the transplanted mid-westerners, Kendall and Hazel Briggs. Ken was an engineer who flew Piper Cubs for fun, smoked a rather British-looking briar pipe, wore tweed knickers and plaid flannel shirts and had an Irish Setter named Ginger. Hazel, his wife, was a slim, dark-haired woman with an irresistibly optimistic smile who made roast chicken Sunday dinners and baked apple pies that she'd set to cool on her window sill beneath her calico curtains.

Al's future office-mate, Bill Verlin, was a tight-lipped Irishman who was destined for dental school. Bill drank his scotch from shot glasses like a movie cowboy and sang with a deep-throated baritone voice. As a third-generation Irish-man, he had already integrated himself into the American culture and was, for my father, yet another connection to the mainstream culture of the U.S.A. Al and Bill met when they double-dated with my mother and her school chum, May.

As a teenager in the late 1920's, Al imagined himself becoming a doctor, perhaps a world-famous eye surgeon. He did not anticipate the Great Depression, which began just as he was about to apply to medical school. Al had the brains and the motivation, but not the money for medical school. His parents were poor, and student loans and scholarships were very few and far between then. And so he had to settle for two years in chiropody school. It was a disappointment he never got over and all his life he looked longingly at his doctor friends, envying not only their prestigious positions in the community and their seemingly unlimited incomes, but their ability to heal people. Instead he tended to people with bunions and ingrown toenails and skin diseases. He could not operate on his patients. And, especially during the Depression, so few of his patients had much money, he found it difficult to charge them much more than a minimum fee or sometimes none at all. He agonized when he felt he had to raise his fee by so much as a dollar, and dreaded losing them.

Renee and Al courted for several years before they made it official at the altar of the little below-ground-level church of Our Lady of the Assumption. As it turned out, Renee and her sisters had all been a bit spoiled by the Sofia notion that their generation of Italian-American girls didn't really have to learn to cook or sew or do housework because they were going to inherit the American Dream and marry wealthy American aristocrats and be waited on hand-and-foot by servants for the rest of their lives.

On the other hand, when Al's mother learned that Renee could barely boil pasta water, Rosa was not pleased. She volunteered to teach her how to make some basic Italian dishes, but of course, the language barrier made that difficult. And so the chore fell to my father, to his sister, Rose, and to Renee's own mother, Grandma Sofia. Grandma Sofia was one of those calm, quietly unassuming cooks who knew instinctively how to bring out the very essence of flavor in just about anything she cooked without a lot of fuss and fancy sauces. And she was as good at all-American pot roast as she was at pasta e fagoli.

Evidently my mother learned quickly from her various teachers because by the time I was old enough to know lasagna from baked macaroni, people were raving about her cooking the way they raved about Grandma Sofia's. Mom was even brave enough after a few years married to Al to cook Sunday dinners for his family, and her marinara sauce passed their culinary muster with flying colors. But Renee Mariani was not to be seduced by all that "Eye-talian" acclaim for her mastery of Italian cuisine. She also learned from her mother the rules of basic American cooking, and did not hesitate to serve the Mariani clan her very own mouth-watering Yankee-style rib roast, or roast beef with Yorkshire pudding.

I suppose you could say that ultimately, it was at the dinner table that the first and second generation of Italian-Americans in our family finally reached out to embrace each other on equal terms, and that it was in the kitchen that the line between those generations all but disappeared.

VJ DAY.

By Rob Mariani

The news came in from the Pacific on our little plastic kitchen radio just after breakfast. Phones began ringing all up and down Campbell Drive and throughout the Country Club neighborhood, all over the Bronx and the rest of America.

By 9 AM, my father and I were out in his green Oldsmobile leading a small caravan of cars through the leafy summer streets, up Agar Place, over to Waterbury Avenue, past Providence Rest, where the old ladies were carefully stored, then back down along Country Club Road past the Villa Maria Academy for Girls with its cloistered walls and whispering nuns. Horns blaring, we were the automotive equivalent of Paul Revere, only it was not the British who were coming—it was the Japanese who were going.

I sat on the front seat next to my father, my feet not touching the floor, as we wheeled crazily around corners, bumping over curbstones. I wondered what had gotten into this man who usually drove with such precision and care.

"The War is over!" he hollered out the window into the damp, hot August air, and people who had just heard the news on their radios came out of their houses and cheered us as if we were the returning army, the conquering heroes of World War II.

After a while, my father's hand got sore from pounding on the horn and he un-screwed the disk that housed the honking mechanism and fixed it so the horn blew continuously all by itself. It was a harsh, angry sound like a cry coming from deep in the chest. When I looked at the expression on my father's face, I was reassured that this was truly the sound of joy.

American flags of all sizes suddenly appeared everywhere like spangled blossoms blooming in the summer's swelter. The flags fluttered from car aerials and window sills, flag poles and handlebars.

Block parties broke out like bonfires on front porches and street corners. When we returned home, our front stoop at 3305 Campbell Drive was the scene of one of these parties. Kegs of beer and platters of food which had been carefully hoarded and rationed through the dark winter of the War, appeared now in abundance, and the brick front of our four-family house was festooned with red, white and blue crepe paper.

There was literally dancing in the streets. Someone brought out a radio and blasted the pop music of the day interspersed with celebratory newscasts that kept reassuring us that indeed the War was at an end.

A few streets over from us, we could see the pink-white fireballs from a Roman candle arc across the darkening sky. Uncles (and all the men we called "Uncle") who were home on furlough, arrived in their uniforms. "Uncle" Willie, a young First Lieutenant who had survived the Battle of the Bulge, was crying openly as he danced with every woman there, twirling them around and around on the sidewalk.

Then, to dazzle us kids, he put a burning cigarette out on his tongue, laughed and swallowed the gray ashes, washing them down with a swig of Ballantine's Ale from a can. And he did it again and again, every time we asked him to, until his wife, Honey, made him stop.

As darkness continued to fall, an iridescent air force of lightening bugs emerged from the wooded lot across the street and from our backyard forsythia bushes that grew around our Victory Gardens. The party frenzy intensified and people got drunker and sillier and louder and happier and the lightning bugs did their incandescent aerobatics all around us. My friends and I ran around frantically catching the bugs as fast as we could with our hands as their little greenish yellow tail lights winked on and off. They were easy to capture because they flew so slowly, hovering like miniature helicopters, and holding their light for almost two seconds against the blue-black sky. We put them in a jar with a few spears of grass for comfort and punched holes in the metal jar lid for air. In no time, I had imprisoned a dozen or more and I ran to the porch to show the adults my prizes. But in the glare from the porch light, the bugs became dull and as ordinary as any other insect. So I ran back into the dark to admire them in their element.

In a few more weeks, my mother would deliver my baby brother, John. She was large and uncomfortable and nervous in the close heat. The revelers were tossing empty beer cans and liquor bottles over the sides of the porch where they were piling up under our kitchen window.

Suddenly Uncle Willie came over to us where we were playing with our lightening bugs. He picked me up and flung me over his shoulder and began dancing around crazily, then he tossed me up in the air and I thought for a moment he was going to let me hit the ground, but at the last second he caught me and twirled me around again. It scared me so much and I was so tired from the long day of non-stop revelry that I started to cry and couldn't stop. My mother came over and took me into the house and laid me on my bed with the window fan humming in the window. I was till crying and trying to catch my breath. My limbs ached and I rolled around on the cool sheets. My mother turned the light out. The sounds of the people partying outside became all one sound.

"Where are my lightning bugs?" I whimpered. My mother placed the jar on the dresser and sat down beside me, patting my head with her cool hand. The jar of lightning bugs was like a small lighthouse in the dark room. There was a rhythm to their silent blinking that soothed me and gradually I dropped off to sleep.

When I woke up the next morning, the weather was already becoming a precise duplicate of the previous day's— hot and steamy with the cicada buzz in the bushes out back. The most momentous day in the history of the world had just passed. A day on which adults had turned into rowdy children and I had been there to see it all. I don't know what I expected things to be like now, the day after, but I was disappointed that everything seemed so much the same. Perhaps I thought the sun would rise in a different place in the sky and shadows would be cast upwards instead of downwards across the streets. Perhaps I expected that *I'd* be a different person living in a different house with new parents, starting all over on a fresh, rain-rinsed day.

In the next room I could hear my father shifting his weight in bed and my mother's shallow breathing. She sighed.

I looked down at the foot of my bed. The jar of lightning bugs stood on my dresser, but there was no sign of life in it now, only the wilted spears of grass. I looked closer and saw at the bottom of the jar, one barely alive firefly on his back, his legs pointing skyward, wriggling almost imperceptibly. His pale green torso pulsed once more and then was still in the rapidly expanding light of yet another American summer day.

MOZZ IN WATER.

By John Mariani

To be an Italian in the Bronx in the early '50s seemed the greatest thing in the world. The Yankees dominated baseball and the Yankees were dominated by players with names like DiMaggio, Rizzuto and Berra. No one rode a horse faster than Eddie Arcaro. The heavyweight champ of the world was Rocky Marciano, a pug who resembled Fiorello LaGuardia, was built like Mount Vesuvius, and had a fearsome right hand like a ten-pound hammer that he used to pummel his opponents to the canvas. Jake LaMotta, the Middleweight champ who could take a vicious beating, sap a guys' strength, then put him through the ropes, lived among us, in a brick house over on Pelham Parkway, and we'd see him out in the front yard with his gorgeous young blonde wife, Vicki, waving at us as we drove by and honked our horn. If we were lucky, he'd do a little mock shuffle, like he'd hit us if we got out of the car.

We even had an Italian mayor-- the first since LaGuardia—although Vincent "the Imp"' Impelletteri was no more than a political hack, better at attending clambakes than running the city. He was a Tammany appointee, after the former Tammany mayor, an Irishman named Bill O'Dwyer, took an appointment as Ambassador to Mexico rather than face corruption charges in New York. Anyway, the Imp was beaten badly in the next election by Bob Wagner, who stayed mayor throughout our entire childhood and adolescence.

We had better, truer heroes to look up to, to emulate and to flaunt in the faces of people who thought we were just ditch diggers and spaghetti eaters. What of Arturo Toscanini, the impossibly demanding perfectionist whose work on television, starting in 1948, made him the most famous conductor in the world? He was a master interpreter of Debussy, Strauss, and Beethoven, and he had heroically refused to play under the Nazi and Fascist regimes in the 1930s, moving to New York where the NBC orchestra was created in 1937 just for him. People who had never seen a conductor in action, except in Hollywood movies, watched this intense little Italian with the white hair and mustache on television, and it was an image you'd never forget. He was short-sighted and couldn't read the score from the rostrum, so he'd memorize every note and conduct entirely from memory.

Toscanini was a particular hero in our house, not only for his supreme virtuosity but for the unalloyed passion and emotion he brought to the music of Italian and non-Italian composers alike. My father used to love to tell the story of how Toscanini, frustrated by a famous Wagnerian soprano who kept missing her cues, rushed to the music stand, grabbed her by her enormous bosoms, and screamed, "If these were only brains!"

My mother even bought my father a baton so that he could stand in the middle of our living room and conduct Puccini's "Turandot" or Beethoven's Third, imitating Toscanini's every thrust, calming the brass, bringing the violins to a feverish pitch, and holding the orchestra in his arms as he brought them through the finale.

Then there was Ezio Pinza, the handsome, patrician

baritone who took Broadway audiences by storm with his performance in Rodgers and Hammerstein's "South Pacific" in 1950. My parents saw the show five times, and my father, who loved to be told he looked a bit like Pinza, would conduct the music at parties as his dentist friend Bill Verlin sang "Some Enchanted Evening" at the top of his lungs.

A younger, even more handsome Italian was Alfred Arnold Cocozza, a Philadelphia kid who took the stage name Mario Lanza and became a Hollywood tenor, even playing Caruso himself onscreen in 1951.

The Hit Parade was full of Italian voices-- Sinatra, Como, LaRosa, Damone, and a few who had Anglicized their names, like Bennett (born Tony DeBenedetto) and Martin (Dino Martino). Julie LaRosa had an enormous hit with an old Neapolitan gimmick song called "Eh Cumpari," sung in dialect and incomprehensible to just about everyone. Tony Bennett's big hit "Rags to Riches" became an Italian-American immigrant's anthem, and Dean Martin's "When the Moon Hits Your Eye Like a Big Pizza Pie, That's Amore" was a joyous expression of everything that was good and beautiful about being an Italian.

With his perfectly cut black hair slicked back over his ears and curls tumbling down his forehead, his thick eyebrows and dark eyes, a nose like a Roman boxer's, his dark Sicilian complexion, full mouth and gleaming white teeth, Dean Martin played off the Jewish-American schlemiel comedy of his partner Jerry Lewis, and when Dean started to sing in a voice that was deep, husky, smooth, seductive and gay, American women in the 1950s went crazy, the way they had over Sinatra a decade before.

Other Italian singers like Jerry Vale milked "That's Amore" for its sentimentality and made it sappy. They exaggerated the Italian words, blubbered through the lyrics, swayed back and forth like gorillas, and played the dumb dago to the hilt.

But Dean Martin knew how to inflect the song with just enough lilt, throwing in a few extra vowels, playing with the song's lyrics but putting them over with exuberance and brio so that it made people listening to him wish they were Italian.

"When the moon hits your eye like a big pizza pie,

That's amore.

When the stars make you drool just-a like pasta fazool,

That's amore.

'Scooza me, but you see,

Back in old Napoli, that's amore!"

In the candy stores, factories and living rooms, the radios blared pop music--girl ballads like Jo Stafford's "You Belong to Me," Gogi Grant's "The Wayward Wind" and Patti Page's "The Tennessee Waltz." A cute Irish girl named Rosemary Clooney had major hits doing mock-Italian songs with names like "Batcha-Me" and "Come On-a My House," whose lyrics held out the sweet, salacious promise of "figs and things" and . . . "everything."

Every Italian could sing and did sing, and street corners in the Bronx were stages for what later came to be called "do-wop" groups, trios and quartets whose intricate, wailing a cappella renditions of old standards and new music formed the basis of what was to become urban rock-and-roll. Many of these groups became famous, and one of the most famous of them all came from the Belmont section of the Bronx, after which they took their name-- Dion & The Belmonts. Their biggest hits drew on puberty's quivering plaints like "Why Must I Be a Teenager in Love?" The do-wop groups competed with each other for the sweetest sound, the most soulful lament and the most intricate scat line, like the Belmonts' dazzlingly baroque "Wop! Wop! Wop-bop-a-looma-awop-bang-bang" on "I Wonder Why."

37

There was always music in the air around Belmont, which was largely Neapolitan, isolated to this day from the blight that began to encroach on Fordham in the '50s. From the windows came the strains of old Neapolitan folk songs like "O sole mio!" and "Torna a Surriento" played on old phonographs and wooden radios. Most of these songs were unrelievedly melancholy, many of them expressing despair at never seeing Naples again. Others were tied to great moments in Neapolitan history, like "Funiculi, Funicula," which commemorated the opening of a railway up the side of Mount Vesuvius.

All of these were known and sung by the vendors along Arthur Avenue, which, crisscrossed by 187th Street, formed the heart of Belmont. This was where all the food stores were-- the pasta shops, the cheese shops, the pizzerias, meat and seafood markets, fruit and vegetable stands. Every vendor sang as he worked, plopping lemons into a paper bag to the waltz time of "Santa Lucia." Another would croon the lilting refrain of "Oj Mari" while slicing prosciutto on a machine-- back and forth, back and forth, as he looked across the counter at a pretty girl. He would gently take a thin slice and place it daintily in her hand, shaking his head back and forth and singing, "Quanta suonno ca perdo per te"-- "I have lost so much sleep over you."

All along Arthur Avenue the air smelled like garlic and tomato, fresh basil, the aroma of pizza from Mario's, where all the New York Yankees came to eat, and the inebriating smell of breads baking in the ovens of Addeo & Sons and Madonia Brothers.

There was also the stench of the live poultry market, where children goaded each other to enter, hold their noses, and force themselves to watch the slaughter of the screeching chickens and rabbits. The owner would tie their legs with a string, slit the neck and cut down through the chest and stomach as the rabbit's high-pitched squeal rang through the stinking room. You could see the steam come out of the innards and the guts glistening with clean, warm blood.

Although my family lived several miles from Arthur Avenue, my father would go there almost every Thursday afternoon, when he finished his office hours early.

For him it was a return to his old neighborhood, for he'd grown up on Cambrelling Avenue, just off Arthur Avenue, and, though his people had come from the province Abruzzi on the Adriatic, he understood and enjoyed hearing the Neapolitan melodies as he shopped among the vendors. He'd double park the Chevy, signal the most proximate vendor where he'd be in case anyone had to get out, then go into the salumeria to buy some prosciutto, which he demanded be sliced thin enough "so I could read Il Progresso through it." Then next door to Madonia Brothers for an enormous round loaf of crusty Italian bread straight out of the oven.

While the girl wrapped the bread in white paper and tied it with a string, he'd point to the light, wafer-like biscuits called savoiardi and say he'd take a dozen.

Last stop was the cheese shop to buy a fresh mozzarella in water. Heavy, creamy and glistening, with the heft and shape of a woman's breast, the mozz were kept in salted water to keep them fresh. My father would specify which one he wanted, and the woman would ladle it out into a piece of waxed paper, then place it in a paper carton.

By the time my father arrived home, I'd already had lunch. If it was during the school year, the bread, prosciutto and mozz would be my snack at three o'clock. But in summer, I waited for my father to arrive back at our apartment at around two o'clock, and I'd always ask, "Did you bring some mozz home?" and he'd kid around, scrunch up his face like he was going to say he'd forgotten, then bring out the bag from behind his back.

He'd take off his jacket and hat and lay them on the living room couch. Then he'd turn on the Victrola and put a 78 RPM record on the turntable. It would be Toscanini, conducting "Capriccio Italienne" or Carmen Cavallaro playing the Toselli Serenade on the piano. Carefully my father would then unwrap the mozz in water, and, with the same surgical precision and gentleness he used in treating his patients, he'd slice the bread thin enough to absorb the flavors of the meat and cheese but thick enough not to turn soggy. He'd unwrap the rosy, salty slices of prosciutto that had been laid out in impeccably neat layers between sheets of paper so that the slices didn't stick to one another. With a fork, he would then deftly curl back a single slice of prosciutto. The light would shine through it. He cut into the yellow-white mozz that oozed milk and beaded up. It was still a little warm when you bit into it, and the flavors were the same week after week.

My father would sit there in his shirt and tie, drinking a beer with his meal. I ate slowly, stretching out the time, and we talked about nothing in particular. But I always felt closer to him on those days than at any other time in my life. He would sit at the kitchen table, bite off a morsel of his sandwich, take a sip of beer, then close his eyes and raise his hand. "Listen," he said very softly, as Toscanini lulled the orchestra into a slow, sad movement. "That's very. . . very Italian."

MAMA-NUN.

By Rob Mariani

The Spring that I was five, my mother took me to visit Mama-Nunn, her grandmother, and my great grandmother. It was the Saturday before Easter after a long, dark, dreary Lent. The house on Pilgrim Avenue. where Mama-Nunn lived with her unmarried daughter, Emma, was only a few neighborhoods away from ours, but we didn't go there often because Mama-Nun was very old and always ill.

As we turned the corner onto Mama-Nun's street, everything seemed to age a hundred years.

The women who walked along the sidewalks were diminutive, bow-legged creatures who moved like doddering sparrows. Wrapped in black from head to foot, only their dark, piercing eyes were visible above their scarves. The men wore somber, ashen colors, too-- heavy wool suits with vests. A few wore straw hats but most had black felt fedoras or homburgs, the brims pulled down as if to assure anonymity. Pilgrim Avenue was lined with a tunnel of ancient elm trees that were just getting ready to blossom.

Mama-Nun's was the only stucco house on the block. All the rest were newer, two-and three-family wooden tenements. Hers had been built by her two sons who were professional plasterers and hod-carriers. Her house was trimmed in black and with its pointed, wimple-shaped gable, it reminded me of a giant, gray-faced nun.

Two low, tightly trimmed hedges framed the cement pathway leading to the front steps. A pair of placid white concrete lions guarded either side of the path. Going up the steps I felt the weak spring sunshine warming my back and shoulders. My mother's hand guided me towards the front door where My Great Aunt Emma was waiting to greet us. Aunt Emma's face looked like a pale moon against the dark interior of the house. The air smelled as if it had been scrubbed clean with brown lye soap and rubbed with furniture polish.

In the hallway there was a large old, hand-tinted photograph of Papa-Nun, my great grandfather who had lived to be 92. I had a very vague memory of Papa-Nun sitting on the front steps of the house, a round, white-haired man with a huge snowy handlebar mustache. In the photo he was wearing a wide-brimmed straw hat with a big white feather tucked into the band. All I could think of when I looked at the photograph was St. Peter as he would look at the gate of heaven the day I came to be admitted.

Beneath Papa-Nun's portrait, there were several other photos of aunts and uncles, many of whom I did not recognize. Still, I could see the Girolamo family resemblance in almost all of them-- the high foreheads and slightly spreading nostrils that characterized my mother's mother's side of the family. And the graceful, expressive eyebrows. All the women in the pictures seemed to have those wondrous eyebrows. And they all wore big round hats adorned with blood red roses or cloud-colored nesting doves sewn into them. Around their shoulders, foxes and minks raced endlessly, tail-in-mouth-tail-in-mouth.

Aunt Emma was the daughter who'd stayed behind to care for her parents in their dotage. She never married. And she never complained. Her brothers married and started a plastering business and moved to other parts of the Bronx. Alvina, Emma's older sister, my grandmother, had been married off to Charlie Sofia.

Emma was alone now with Mama-Nun.

As she bent down to press her cheek against mine, her skin felt as cold as marble, like the statues at church that I'd surreptitiously reached through the altar bars to feel.

"How's Mama-Nun, Aunt Emma?" my mother asked, closing the creaking door behind us.

"Oh, she had a pretty good night but her chest is very heavy. She has trouble breathing."

"What did the doctor say?"

Aunt Emma shrugged, "He says she's ninety-nine years old."

"I wanted her to see Robby. It's been a long time. Do you think she remembers him? He was just a baby the last time."

"Her memory comes and goes now," Emma said, ushering us into the front room.

"We keep it a little dark in the house. Mama-Nun doesn't like too much light. It hurts her eyes."

Emma spoke in a hushed voice, as if she were in church. And there were so many religious pictures and statues around, I felt as though I should speak in a whisper too.

"I'll just leave Robby here with you for a bit while I go out shopping and he can visit with Mama-Nun until I come back," my mother said. "Go with Aunt Emma now, honey, go see your great grandma," she urged.

I hung back, burying my face in my mother's hip. Then I felt Aunt Emma's cool hand pulling me gently away. Her grip was easy and soft and reassuring, like her voice, and I gradually relaxed my hold on my mother's thigh and went with her.

"Stay with me, Robert," she said in her saint-like voice. "Mommy will be back soon. Come, I'll take you in to see Mama-Nun. Did you know she's ninety-nine years old?"

I did not think that anyone could be that old and I was torn between leaving my mother and going to see this old, old woman who everyone in the family said would probably even live to be one hundred.

The hallway leading to Mama-Nun's room was hung with ornately framed pictures of angels and saints and a staring Jesus whose fingers pointed alarmingly to his chest where his heart burned like a swollen red tongue. At the end of the shadowy hall there was a big double door. Aunt Emma slid it open slowly and led me into the back parlor where Mama-Nun stayed during the day.

The room was even darker than the rest of the house and at first all I could see was a heap of mushroom-colored, velvet pillows on an overstuffed brown sofa. As I inched closer, the pile of pillows stirred and parted and a tiny, squirrel-like face peeped out. It was a face the size of a walnut, mapped with deep wrinkles and creases like a nut-shell. I stopped abruptly and started to back away, but I felt the gentle bump of Aunt Emma's knee in the small of my back again.

"It's all right, honey," she said pressing me forward into the room. "It's Mama-Nun. See? Mama-Nun? You awake, Mama? Look who I brought to see you. It's your great grandson, Robert. Remember Robert, Mama?"

The old woman's coal-black eyes darted frantically around the room and then fell on me, fixing me with an intense, terrified stare.

A few stringy wisps of gray hair hung down wildly alongside her quivering jaw. She opened her caved-in mouth and I could see one yellow, bone-like tooth in front and the

44

glint of gold farther back in her mouth. With her hooked nose and dry, ruined lips, she looked just like a witch from the movies. A rush of strange, unintelligible words began to emanate from her mouth, filling the heavy, lightless air.

Although she'd been in America for most of her long, long adult life now, Mama-Nun had never learned to speak in English sentences. Instead she spoke some rumbling version of Italian distorted by the seemingly uncontrollable movement of her lower jaw, her phlegm-filled throat, and her constant gasping for breath. I had heard my aunts and uncles speaking a soft, musical Italian, or a loud, comical Italian, but *this* sound coming from Mama-Nun was full of harsh, crow-like noises and animal grunts and serpentine hisses. Her bony gums clacked together between words and there was a desperate wheezing sound way down in her chest.

I concluded that Mama-Nun must have been the oldest living person in the world and that she was struggling for breath because she'd used all hers up, and now to survive, she had to steal the breath from other people.

In the far corner of the parlor, a red vigil light flickered at the foot of a statue of the Virgin Mary. The calm-eyed saint stood on the globe with her palms turned outward, gazing down at her bare feet. A plaster serpent with an apple in its mouth writhed around her naked ankles.

Mama-Nun's wheezing filled the room now. The air was thick with it and pressing against my chest. When I tried to inhale, Mama-Nun seemed to be drawing the breath back from me, sucking it down into her own starved lungs from across the room. A terrifying honking sound began coming from her fragile chest. I felt panic as I searched the room for a crack of light, a breath of air. The red vigil light flickered casting dancing shadows on the ceiling, in tempo with Mama-Nun's harsh, laborious breathing.

Now she pointed her talon-like finger right at me. Her age-spotted hand was wrapped in a string of black rosary beads, which in the dim light looked like a trail of crawling ants.

"Emma! Emma!" Mama-Nun croaked, her voice like an iron file against raw wood.

Aunt Emma's round face appeared like a pearl above me. Mama-Nun began to cough violently and Aunt Emma went to her. The entire room seemed to swell and contract with the old woman's gasping. I knew that she was coming to take my very last breath.

From her apron pocket, Aunt Emma produced a small bottle of mahogany colored liquid and poured some into Mama-Nun's gaping wound of a mouth. I saw the snake-like tongue emerge and lick her lips. Almost immediately, the coughing subsided. Aunt Emma cooed over the old lady, soothing her head with her cool, white palms, laying her back down onto the bed among the pile of brown velvet pillows. Slowly the air in the room seemed to grow calmer. My breathing became easier.

Aunt Emma tried to explain to Mama-Nun in soft, soothing Italian who the little boy cringing at her side was.

"It's all right, Mama. It's just little Robert, your great grandson. You remember him."

But Mama-Nun had shut her eyes and was lying back, sinking deeper beneath the pillows. She lay very still, her chest rising and falling beneath her daughter's ministering hands.

"She's asleep," Aunt Emma said, leading me gently away.

We left the room, sliding the heavy door closed behind us. We moved down the dim hallway under the pictures of the saints and the picture of Jesus with his exposed heart still in flames. Emma was leading me towards a square of light at the end of the hall. As we drew nearer, I caught the sweet scent of anisette that I will always associate with Aunt

Emma's immaculate kitchen. The corners of my mouth ached now from trying not to cry, but a tear finally escaped and rolled down my cheek. I tasted it with my tongue. I looked back once down the long hallway, fearing that Mama-Nun might suddenly burst from the shadows and come after me.

Aunt Emma's kitchen was as bright and sparkling as Mama-Nun's room had been dark and oppressive. The weak Easter sunlight outside streamed in through the back windows. It flooded the white tile floor that Emma's brothers had laid tile by tile. It bounced off the white walls, and the spotless, gleaming stove.

The only color was a dish of lemons that stood on the white tablecloth alongside a plate of Aunt Emma's Easter cookies. Thin, delicate wafers in the shapes of stars and moons, crosses and hearts.

"You mustn't be afraid of Mama-Nun, Robert," she said. "She's practically blind now. She couldn't really see who you were. It upset her, that's all, dear."

When Aunt Emma talked, she barely moved her lips. I stared at how carefully she had wound her dark braid of hair around her head. It reminded me of a crown of thorns. I had never seen her with her hair in any other arrangement. I wondered if anyone had.

Stout and matronly, Aunt Emma had been middle-aged since she'd turned fifteen. I don't think I'd ever seen her without an apron on. Her features were small and her dark brown eyes were set wide apart. Some-times her right eye seemed to wander off all by itself. She looks like a saint, I thought to myself. Saint Emma.

"Here, dear, have a cookie." She held out a thin white crescent moon shape to me the way I'd seen a picture of Saint Francis doing as he fed the birds in the snow. Then she poured me a tiny glassful of ruby colored wine. It was so sweet and syrupy that at first I thought it was cough medicine.

I bit into the cookie and let the sugary crumbs melt on my tongue, slowly coating my mouth in almost the same way that the flat, round communion wafer did.

I don't think Mama-Nun made it to 100. She must have died soon after my visit, probably later that spring. I was too young to attend her funeral but I remember my mother getting dressed to go to it, her head and half of her face draped in a black transparent veil. I never had another great grandmother, but I can't say I regret that. One Mama-Nun has really been enough to last me a lifetime.

WHITE DREAMS.

By Rob Mariani

When the blizzard of 1948 hit the East Coast, I was eight years old. And unlike other more benign snowstorms I'd experienced, this one was delivered from the sky in shovelsful. It began about a week before Christmas right after lunch one Saturday and the entire world came to a stand-still for several days.

My father stopped going to work and moped around the house doing crossword puzzles and almost willingly framing pictures and fixing shelves for my mother. Several times a day he would go to the snow-lit front window, look out wistfully at what used to be our driveway and shake his head.

My mother settled in on the sofa to string popcorn and sew presents that the drifting snow kept us from going out to buy. By some miracle, the Christmas tree had been purchased early that year, and we dragged it up the cellar stairs and installed it in the center of the living room one afternoon as the snow continued to rage outside. At night we stared out the frosted windows into the December darkness and the tree lights were reflected in the black glass giving the impression that there was a twin of our tree floating, fully lit, several feet above the ground in the front yard.

After the snow finally stopped falling, the wind sculpted it into six and seven-foot high drifts, casting great white mountainsides up against the houses, the porches, and cars.

Then the temperature dropped and everything froze. Suspended animation.

My father's green Oldsmobile was buried up to its roof by garbage trucks armed with snowplows. They came whirling through the night like earth-bound Valkyries, hurling sparks, and showers of snow everywhere.

Driving became a memory and our car just another shapeless mound of white outside our kitchen window. After a day or two, my brother and I began treating the Olds' as part of the landscape, immovable, locked in ice like some Detroit dinosaur. With complete irreverence, we built a snow fort on its roof, sliding down the windshield and hood like Eskimo children. (Glancing up from this activity one time, I caught a glimpse of my father in the kitchen window watching us. Concerned but strangely silent in the face of all this blank whiteness, he turned away as if preferring not to see that we had transformed his car into an Alpine ski jump.)

The blizzard meant no school, of course, early vacation with more time to agonize over the glacial movement of the days towards December 25th, that miraculous date which seemed to blaze like a Yule log on the last pages of every calendar.

We cheered the snow as it poured down on us like torn circus tickets, exhorting it to overpower school buses and obliterate roads. It simply could not snow enough for us. The higher it piled against the buildings and cars, the longer school would be postponed (perhaps all the way until summer vacation!), and the better the sledding.

The sledding. It became an occupation for us, with every hill, every driveway, every pile of drifted snow an irresistible bobsled run. And although the hours of daylight were short, each day seemed almost endless and we did not mind the bite of the bitter wind, even when it blew fistfuls of sharp-edged flakes directly into our muffler-covered faces.

Little ice balls clung in clusters to our mittens, and we chewed them off so that we could keep our hands securely on the steering bars of our Flexible Flyer and Speedaway sleds as we careened down endless hills again and again and again. There was no respite.

One night, some of the older kids ripped a big metal Coke sign off the side of Rosenberg's drugstore and curled the front end of it up in a scroll like a toboggan. They tied a rope to it and waited in the shadows by the bus stop on Campbell Drive until the bus came lumbering up the snow-clogged street. The moment it huffed to a brief halt to discharge a few chilly passengers, the kids rushed out and hitched their handmade sled to the bus's bumper. The metal sign held eight or nine teenagers in tandem as they flew screaming and laughing over frozen streets, sparks flying beneath them when ever the sign struck bare spots where the pavement showed through.

This was the winter that Dicky Lynch broke his leg leading a train of nine sleds (which we inexplicably referred to as a "Tally-Ho") down an ice-encrusted slope we'd christened "Suicide Hill." With the toes of his black rubber galoshes held fast in the sled behind him, Dicky made too sharp a turn around a young Scotch pine. The rest of the train kept going straight, pretzel-ing Dicky's leg around the tree.

But the frenzy of our sledding, the sheer madness of flying down a snowy hill at breakneck speed and then running breathlessly to the top to do it again was so intense and satisfying, that we scarcely noticed Dicky's cries of pain or his oddly bent leg as his brothers carried him off the hill using his Flexible Flyer for a stretcher.

We were already preparing for the next train of sleds,

the next Tally-Ho, this time with *twelve* sleds.

And so the time went during the aftermath of the blizzard. Sledding became our obsession. So many winters with just a dusting of snow had made us treasure these days of serious sledding. When a new and more dangerous hill was discovered, as it was almost everyday, we flocked to it like snow-crazed blackbirds to breadcrumbs.

And no matter how late I left the hills at night, there were always the shouts of other kids who had come earlier that morning and who were staying later. Their cries of excitement rang in my ears as I trudged unwillingly home along Campbell Drive beneath the trembling street lamps, pulling my sled like a reluctant dog behind me, the metal clasps on my galoshes jingling. And though completely exhausted, with my cheeks burning now from hours of exposure to the stinging wind, I would have to fight off the urge to return to the hill for just one more perfect run-- the run for which all the other runs had been mere practice.

At home in bed after a warm supper and a bath, my toes deliciously defrosted beneath the sheets, I turned my wind-burned face against the snowy expanse of my pillow and slept. And I dreamed I was at the very top of a high, high snow-swept mountain looking down into the white bowl of a valley with its tiny toy houses and winking lights like the ones on an electric train layout.

I lay my dream sled down before me like a pallet and climbed on top of it, my lips brushing the cold metal steering frame, tasting the steel. Then, slowly, I pushed myself gently over the edge with both hands.

Down I swooped, sliding deeper and deeper into sleep, bouncing over the glistening white hummocks on the ride I'll remember forever and against which I would measure all other rides, down through the seemingly endless progression of hills and winters that could never be as long or as cold or as white or as wonderful as this, the Winter of winters.

CHRISTMAS IN THE BRONX.

By John Mariani

Maybe it didn't snow for Christmas every year in the Bronx back in the '50s. But my memory of at least one perfect snow-bound Christmas Eve makes me think it did often enough that I still picture my neighborhood as white as Finland in those days when I lived along the choppy waters of the Long Island Sound.

But for all the decorations and the visits to stores and Rockefeller Center, it was the sumptuous Christmas feasts that helped maintain our families' links to the Old Country long after most other immigrant traditions had faded away. Food was always central to everyone's thoughts at Christmas, and the best cooks in each family were renowned for specific dishes no one else dared make.

The assumption that everything would be exactly the same as last year was as comforting as knowing that Christmas Day would follow Christmas Eve. The finest ancestral linens were ironed and smoothed into place, dishes of hard candy were set out on every table, and the kitchen ovens hissed and warmed our homes for days. The reappearance of the old dishes, the irresistible aromas, tastes and textures, even the seating of family members in the same spot at the table year after year anchored us to a time and a place that was already changing more rapidly than we could understand.

It's funny now to think that my memories of the food and the dinners are so much more intense than those of toys and games I received, but that seems true of most people. The exact taste of Christmas cookies, the sound of beef roasting in its pan, and the smell of evergreen mixed with the scent of cinnamon and cloves and lemon in hot cider were like holy incense in church, unforgettable, like the way you remember your parents' faces when they were young.

No one in our neighborhood was poor but few were rich. Yet we mounted feasts as lavish as any I could imagine in a book, and in the days preceding Christmas people took enormous joy in spending their money on foods only eaten during that season.

It was still a time when the vegetable man would sell his produce from an old truck on Campbell Drive, and Dugan's and Krug's bread men came right to your door with special holiday cupcakes and cookies. The butcher on Middletown Road usually carried fresh fish only on Fridays, but he was always well stocked with cod, salmon, lobsters and eel during the holidays. The pastry shops worked overtime to bake special Christmas breads and cakes, which would be gently wrapped in a swaddling of very soft pink tissue paper tied up with ribbons and sometimes even sealed with wax to deter anyone from opening it before Christmas.

By Christmas Eve the stores ran out of everything, and pity the poor cook who delayed buying her chestnuts, ricotta cheese, or fresh yeast until it was too late. Weeks in advance the women would put in their order at the live poultry market for a female rabbit--not a male-- or a goose that had to weigh exactly twelve pounds.

You always knew what people were cooking for

Christmas because the aromas hung in the hallways of the garden apartments and the foyers of their homes-- garlicky tomato sauces, roast turkeys, rich shellfish stews, and the sweet, warm smells of pastries and breads could make you dizzy with hunger. When you went out into the cold, those aromas would slip out the door and mingle with the biting sea-salted air and the fresh wet snow swept in off the Sound.

At the Italian homes in the Bronx ancient culinary rituals were followed long after they'd lost their original religious symbolism. The traditional meatless meal of Christmas Eve-- "La Vigilia"-- which began centuries ago as a form of penitential purification, developed into a robust meal of exotic seafood dishes that left one reeling from the table. According to the traditions of Abruzzi, where my father's family came from, the Christmas Eve dinner should be composed of seven or nine dishes--mystical numbers commemorating the seven sacraments and the Holy Trinity multiplied by three. This was always my Auntie Rose's shining moment. She would cook with the zeal and energy of a dozen nuns, beginning with little morsels of crisply fried calamari. She made spaghetti on a stringed utensil called a *"ghitarra"* and served it with a sauce teeming with shellfish. Next came an enormous pot of lobster *fra diavolo*--a powerful coalescence of tomato, garlic, onion, saffron and hot red peppers, all spooned into soup plates around shiny, scarlet-red lobsters that some guests attacked with daunting, unbridled gusto while others took their dainty time extracting every morsel of meat from the deepest recesses of the body, claws and legs.

Few children would eat *baccala*, a strong-smelling salted cod cooked for hours in order to restore its leathery flesh to edibility, and stewed eel, an age-old symbol of renewal, was a delicacy favored mostly by the old-timers. But everyone waited for the dessert--the yeasty, egg bread called *"panettone,"* shaped like a church dome and riddled with golden raisins and candied fruit.

Christmas Day came too early for everyone but the children, but as soon as presents were exchanged, my mother and grandmother would begin work on the lavish Christmas dinner to be served that afternoon. It was always a mix of regional Italian dishes and American novelties, like the incredibly rich, bourbon-laced egg nog my father insisted on serving *before* my grandmother's lasagna, in which were hidden dozens of meatballs the size of hazelnuts. Then my mother would set down a massive roast beef, brown and crackling on the outside, red as a poinsettia within, surrounded by sizzling roast potatoes and Yorkshire pudding glistening from the fat absorbed from the beef. Dessert reverted to venerable Italian tradition with my grandmother's prune-and-chocolate filled pastries and honeyed cookies called "*struffoli.*"

After such a meal, we needed to go for a walk in the cold air. In other homes up and down our block people were feasting on Norwegian lutefisk, Swedish meatballs, German *stollen*, Irish plum pudding and American gingerbread. If you stopped and listened for a moment, you could hear the families singing carols in their native tongue.

By early evening people got ready to leave and leftovers were packed up to take home, belying everyone's protest that they wouldn't eat for days afterwards.

By then the snow had taken on an icy veneer and the wind died down to a whisper. I remember how the cold air magnified sounds far, far away, so as I crept into bed I could hear the waves lapping the sea wall and the rattling clack-clack, clack-clack of the El running from Buhre Avenue to Middletown Road. It was a kind of lullaby in those days, when it never failed to snow on Christmas in the Bronx.

OLD MAN IN THE TREE.

By Rob Mariani

Someone had made a spring leaf fire and the brown smoke was rising up and smudging the sky over the vacant, tree-tangled lot we called The Rosalyn. "The Rosalyn Estate" was an abandoned piece of real estate once owned by a family of landed gentry from another era. Nobody in the neighborhood seemed to know exactly who they'd been. The Rosalyn consisted of two or three acres of wild shrubs and uprooted trees, bordered on one side by a tumbled down brick wall. The wall separated it from the Villa Maria Academy, a Catholic girls' school where young females were instructed by nuns on the theory and practice of virginity and other virtues. The back side of the plot ran down to a crumbling seawall on Pelham Bay. The front of the lot that ran along Country Club Road, bordered by a tall, unruly hedge that stood a good fifteen feet tall.

In our 10-year-old minds, The Rosalyn was anything but a 'vacant' lot. In fact, it was Sherwood Forest. It was Tarzan's Kingdom of the Apes. It was Venus, Mars and the moon, it was a sprawling Texas prairie where The Lone Ranger and Tonto roamed, looking for beleaguered townspeople to rescue.

On this particular Saturday in April, there was a posse chasing me through the Rosalyn. I loped along the familiar trails where the sepia colored grass grew shoulder-high and the old trees spread their still-bare branches overhead. I could hear the posse behind me-- Richie, Dave and Chris. But I knew they couldn't see me through the thick foliage. I brought my imaginary horse, Bullet, to a halt, confident I'd given my pursuers the slip. I was at the foot of the huge old cherry tree that stood at the edge of an embankment. Last summer, a few of us kids had installed a rope swing on this tree. It was nothing more than a thick length of sturdy line double-knotted at the bottom. You stood on the knot and then launched out off the embankment. The swing would describe a long, downward arc out over the swampy ground below and then ascend again returning the rider to level ground retracing approximately the same glide path. For a few seconds, the ride was about as close as you could get to flying without wings.

I looked up the embankment, which was about 20 feet high, and saw that there was somebody on the swing. As most of my friends were in the posse behind me, I couldn't imagine who this intruder might be and how he would have the audacity to be riding our private swing. It could be Jimmy Burns, I thought, because even though he wasn't from our immediate neighborhood, Jimmy was always horning in on some of our territory lately.

But it wasn't Jimmy. It was an adult. A full-grown man with chalky-colored hair and wearing a maroon bathrobe over light blue pin-striped pajamas. I could see that the man was not clutching the rope with his hands the way we did when we rode the swing. Instead, the man's hands hung limp at his sides and he was not actually swinging but just sway-ing almost imperceptibly in the wind, his chin resting on his chest.

When I noticed that the rope was around the man's neck

and that his eyes were wide open and staring and his skin was an icy blue color, I started running back down the trail yelling. "There's a dead guy on the swing! A *dead* guy... a dead guy!.... on our *swing!* A *dead* guy!"

I looked back once to make sure I hadn't imagined it, but there the man was in his maroon robe with one bedroom slipper dangling from his pale foot, the other lost somewhere in the grass beneath him. His hands hung at his sides in a kind of faint, questioning "why?" gesture. The dead weight of his stillness pulled the branch that held the swing down in a u-shape towards the ground.

The ambulance with its red flashing light drove right up to the edge of The Rosalyn and men in white coats stumbled through the high grass. There were police cars with their radios squawking. They wanted me to show them where the dead man was. But I didn't want to go back into the Rosalyn and have to look at the man's cold blue face or his empty, frozen stare again.

They were saying I didn't have to look at him, only show them where he was. I took them halfway back along the path to the swing and pointed in the direction of the old man. Then I couldn't stop myself from looking and I couldn't help imaging the horrible step-by-step mechanics of what the old man had done. The climbing up onto the box, the tying up of the noose around his neck and the placing of it around his own neck and then the stepping off into thin air.

Hangings were pretty standard stuff in movies of the early 'fifties, but this was nothing like the cinematic versions. This was sinister and frightening and much too real.

I could hear adult conversations all around me. They were using words we usually heard on the radio programs like "The Inner Sanctum," and "Suspense!" The programs that used to send me running from the room when the creepy organ music swelled and the spooky-voiced announcer seemed to be coming right out of the radio's speaker into our livingroom.

At some point it occurred to me that the man might have
been murdered. I pictured him in the half-lit hours of that
Saturday morning with the sky just turning the color of tin
foil, being taken from his bedroom by three husky men in
black overcoats. Like the guys I'd seen in the gangster
movies played by Bogart and Edward G. Robinson. Mob
guys from the South Bronx or maybe up by Tremont Ave.
The old man, only half awake, too confused to cry out, and
the men in coats carrying him to the place in The Rosalyn
where they somehow knew the swing was, hooking him up
by his scrawny neck and pushing him off the embankment. I
saw in my mind, the old man struggling like a choking
chicken, clutching frantically at his throat as the thick rope
drew tight around his neck and the men in the overcoats
retreated through the woods.

But then I saw the crumpled oil can beneath the old
man's feet. He had obviously kicked it out from under
himself. It must have been suicide. A word I'd heard the
Irish Christian Brothers who taught us in 5th grade to refer to
as a mortal sin. It was sin to take one's own life, the brothers
said, because only God had that right. People who killed
themselves ended up in hell for eternity.

All the next night and for many nights afterwards, every
time I closed my eyes, the man was there with his vague,
questioning hand gesture and his blue-white face, his staring,
dead fish eyes, the breeze moving him slightly back and
forth, emphasizing his terrifying stillness. How much stiller
than sleep death is, I thought. And forever.

For the rest of that Spring and on into the Summer, none
of us kids would go anywhere near the swing. It took weeks
before anyone would even venture back into The Rosalyn
again, and then if we heard even so much as a rustle in the
grass we'd run out, terrified that the old man had somehow
come back to life and was stalking us through the underbrush. All of a sudden, the little piece of the world we had

60

once claimed as our own no longer belonged to us.

We diverted ourselves back out on the streets of the neighborhood with noisier, less private activities than the ones we'd practiced in The Rosalyn. Stick ball. Ring-a-Leave-o. Red Rover.

Spring passed and then a drought-plagued summer and the trees all went dry and dormant again. Someone-- everyone suspected Riche Swift-- set fire to The Rosalyn's tangled, tinder-dry foliage. The flames leapt up over the tops of the hedges and rolled through the stiff grasses, each blade igniting like a matchstick. My friends and I stood at the perimeter cheering the fire as it advanced and consumed the swatch of land we had once cherished as our private domain.

It was a while before Davey Cuniff went over to the red fire alarm box on the corner and pulled the lever. By the time the fire trucks arrived, The Rosalyn was a charred ruin, the flames diminished to flickering tongues struggling along the charcoal colored ground. The firemen turned their big hoses on it and in a few minutes there was only smoldering black rubble.

The next week bulldozers arrived to level the lot. They dug deep beneath the charred earth, casting up ancient roots and huge, prehistoric, elephant-shaped boulders. From the sidewalk, we watched with relief as the work crews toppled the old cherry tree where a remnant of our suicide swing still dangled like a limp, black snake.

Once the Roslyn was leveled it was only a matter of weeks before a construction crew rolled in. What arose out of the chaos was a three-story, yellow brick structure with a terracotta tile roof. The new building was a convent that would house an order of Spanish nuns, tiny round women who looked and sounded like nesting sparrows as they hopped and twittered around the newly-planted landscape.

By the time another year went by, the convent was complete and nothing that reminded us of The Roslyn remained.

In a steeple above its red tiled roof, a small church bell rang early every morning calling the nuns to Mass in the dark stone chapel, and in the evenings to vespers. Outside, old bent-backed gardeners pruned and groomed the shrubbery around the building and the entire place took on a sunny, well-kept South-of-the-Border look, all smoothed over and neat.

I found myself trying to imagine what had happened to our rope swing. I pictured it lying beneath the ground rotting away, its fibers turning into gray powder and then into earth itself. Back into non-existence.

In the years ahead, there were more occasions for me to see other dead bodies. Not in trees, but at wakes and funerals, where the deceased had been dressed in neat dark suits or sedate dresses and made-up to look like they were sleeping, with faint, well-rested smiles pressed onto their lips.

At the wakes, there were a few times when I thought I glimpsed beneath the veneer of makeup, that cold, blue-whiteness of the dead man on the swing. But usually the corpses looked like department store mannequins, stiff but benign. Their only real similarity with the old man in the tree was that deep, deep, stillness.

Most important, I was always relieved to see that their hands had been carefully folded in front of them in a kind of relaxed praying pose, with a string of rosary beads twined securely around their hands for good measure, as if to keep their palms from falling apart and making that unforgettably terrifying, *"Why?"* gesture.

LEMONADE.

By John Mariani

There were summer days in the Bronx when you couldn't imagine it could be any hotter anywhere else on earth. We'd read stories of people frying eggs on the pavement and of police horses dropping dead right out on the city streets. There were pictures of it in the papers. The *Journal-American* and the *Mirror* and the *Telegram* and the *Daily News* all printed the obligatory photos of drenched boys standing in front of open fire hydrants and shots of Coney Island so packed with people that it made you feel hotter just to see them. The papers also showed cartoons of thermometers with the mercury shooting out the top and quoted cops about how the heat made some people do terrible things they wouldn't ordinarily do, usually at stoplights and toll stations. One August day all the papers carried a story about a man named Randazzo who turned his car out of the traffic and drove right into the Sound because, he told the reporter, "I just really needed to cool off."

We were luckier than most. Living near the water, we could get a cool briny breeze at night that swept through the screens of our apartment. Otherwise we'd lie there in our beds listening to the whirr of the loud metal fans set on our window ledges. The blades moved the sluggish hot air around from one corner to the other, and our sheets got clammy with sweat. We'd get heat headaches.

The darkness had a palpable, depressing heat to it, and we'd stretch out against the cool wall next to our bed until it got warm from our bodies, then we'd turn away again. We'd hear cars driving along the roads, sounding as if they were going real slow, trying to push through soup. We'd hear people's voices muffled by the hot air, and they sounded angry, never laughing as they did on cool spring nights.

Eventually we'd fall off to sleep, but the worst of it was waking up to the heat again in the morning, the same muggy air, and the incessant sound of cicadas in the weeds. You didn't want to eat. Milk went sour fast.

Of course, we could always go to the Club or the movies or occasionally we'd drive out to Jones Beach. But by August, when the heat seemed to have moved in like a fat relative. There was no real escape from the boredom of routine, and we needed something to break the monotony and to take our minds off the summer.

Starting up a new business in August was not the sort of thing that occurred to most people struggling to breathe, but it seemed to me that I might take a crack at some enterprise that could somehow capitalize on the summer's heat. Obvious though it was, a lemonade stand seemed like a bright idea, untried, as far as I knew, in our neighborhood. I'd seen kids do it on television and there was a pretty good story about it in our second grade reader, *New Friends and Neighbors.* Lemonade stands made for perennial magazine covers, although it seemed they were always picturing stands set up in towns where the kids wore overalls and plaid shirts. Those articles never gave any instructions on how to run such a business, so it was a pretty wide open field in the Bronx and might lead to something bigger. Perhaps I could open one, hire some friends to run others, make them all look more or less the same and sell lemonade that always tasted the same, the way the chocolate chip ice cream always tasted the same at every Howard Johnson in the country. I could imagine my picture in the *Bronx Home News* with the Bronx Borough President, James J. Lyons, sipping a glass of my lemonade, his pinky in the air, while my mother and father stood behind him, their hands on my shoulders, looking on with enormous pride.

Photographic evidence indicated that signs posted on the lemonade stands almost always gave a price of two to five cents, and I didn't think there was a great deal of profit to be made from that. Factoring in the heat and the location I was to choose, I felt strongly that I could push the price to a dime and clean up. If the heat didn't break for another week, I should be rolling in dough, with little cost to myself beyond the stand. It never occurred to me that I'd have to pay for the raw materials that went into making the lemonade. My mother would provide that from the lemons and sugar already in the kitchen. I was certain that my voluntary removal from under her feet would be fair trade for making up enough lemonade for an afternoon's commerce. I was right. Her eyes beamed when I told her I'd be spending the afternoon two blocks away, on the corner of Campbell Drive and Agar Place.

While my mother squeezed lemons into two big clear green glass pitchers, I was down in the cellar figuring out how to build my stand. Without any help in actual construction, I decided that my best bet was to cart over a folding table on my wagon, put a tablecloth over it and start simply. I was able to extract an old oilcloth with a flowery Florida design, which seemed not just appropriate but had eye-catching appeal. I carefully chose an array of glasses and some jelly jars that had cartoon characters on them. Then I called Billy Coyle to enlist him in the project, even though I really just needed him to run back to my house to get more lemonade whenever I ran out. I'd pay him something. I just hadn't decided how much. It would depend on how many trips he'd have to make to replenish our supply. Had I called

Johnny Flaherty, I knew I would have been in for an argument on profit sharing, and that simply wasn't possible with a new business operating on a shoestring.

"I made as much as I could with what I had," my mother said when I came upstairs. "You know, you're going to have a problem keeping this cold. I'll give you some ice cubes, but they won't last forever and I won't have any more for hours."

I didn't think this presented any real logistical problem. "Don't worry," I replied. "I'll keep it in the shade."

I tinkered a little with the sweetness of my mother's decoction, but I thought she'd done a first-rate job. Billy Coyle rang the bell, I loaded him down with some paper napkins and a bag of glasses, I set the table onto the wagon, and we were off up the street.

For the first time all summer, I was ecstatic about the oppressive heat that burned the neighborhood. It was easily 90 degrees, maybe 95, and the sun had that corona that made everything hazy and everyone sweaty. My decision to position the stand on the corner of Campbell and Agar was made after considering several alternatives. Since I couldn't venture very far from the neighborhood and needed quick access to product, I stuck close to home. For a moment I considered setting up right outside the Club itself, but I worried about the competition from the snack stand inside. The main thing Campbell & Agar had going for it was that it was a bus stop, and I knew that people getting off those buses would be dying from the heat and dead thirsty. I couldn't imagine anyone seeing my stand and that glistening pitcher of lemonade and resisting the impulse to buy a glass.

I couldn't have been right-er. I had barely smoothed out the oil cloth and set the glasses in a row when a bus lumbered up Campbell Drive and lunged to a halt at the corner. Three people got off. A man and two women. I knew their faces but not their names, so I put on my friendly neighborhood smile, and spoke one word: "Lemonade?"

One woman paid no attention, but the other was with the man, and he was sweating like a pig. He had his jacket off, his tie hanging out of his jacket pocket, his hat in his hand, and his sweaty undershirt showed through his white business shirt.

"That's not a bad idea," he said, turning to his wife, who made a face that strongly registered her displeasure. She didn't have to say anything to convey her criticism: "You don't know where that stuff comes from."

The man, trying to allay her fears, looked down at me and said, "Where's this stuff come from?"

I thought for a brief second to say that I had made it myself, but I threw my mother into the act in the belief that the woman would trust a mother's recipe over a six-year-old's. "My mom made it. Homemade. Right down the street there."

The woman was clearly not convinced. She rolled her eyes, shrugged and said to her husband, "Go ahead if you want it. I'm not that thirsty."

The man seemed really relieved. "O.K., gimme a glass."

I was thrilled. It had all gone according to plan and so flawlessly. I saw money signs, bigger stands, friends congratulating me and a flashbulb going off as the Borough President held up a glass of Mariani's Luscious Lemonade. I slowly poured the lemonade into the man's glass, right to the brim. "How much?" he asked.

"Ten cents," I replied.

"A little high, isn't it? This better be great lemonade."

I had a momentary attack of panic. I saw a vision of the man spitting out the lemonade and screaming to the whole neighborhood that this was undrinkable swill--although people in the Bronx didn't know what swill was-- and that he would expose me as a fraud. An exorbitantly priced fraud at that. I wondered if I could be arrested for selling crappy lemonade.

He took a sip and said, "Hmm." His eyebrows went up and his lips puckered. Then he chugged the rest of it down. "Not bad," he said. "Pretty good. Yeah, that's worth a dime." Then, turning to his wife, he said, "You shoulda gotten one. It's really pretty good."

The man seem transformed by my lemonade. He walked upright. His clothes seemed to dry out before me. He put his hat back on his head. "'S'good lemonade, kid," he said as he walked down Agar.

My day was made. Even if I didn't earn another slim dime, I felt the triumphant charge of a man onto a no-lose proposition. The world of lemonade was there for me to conquer. I was so delirious I reached into my pocket where I kept some change and gave Billy Coyle a nickel. I was feeling flush.

As the afternoon wore on, more buses stopped and more people bought my lemonade. Nobody complained about the price, everyone went away happy, and I was on top of the world. I felt as resourceful as Horatio Alger, who wrote books nobody in our neighborhood had ever read about kids who made successes of their lives through pluck and luck. I obviously had the pluck. If luck came too, so much the better. But men of my vision didn't really need it. We just came by good ideas naturally.

About that time Billy's mother stuck her head out of the house a block away and called for him to come home. Reluctant as he was to leave a burgeoning business, Billy did as he was told--maybe he thought he could enlist his mother in making Mariani's lemonade and thereby increase our source of supply. So Billy said he'd see me tomorrow and left me alone at the stand.

It was just then that I realized I'd run out of glasses. I couldn't leave the stand, especially with the sound of a bus in the distance coming up Campbell Drive. It was now four o'clock--peak period for sales. I thought hard and enjoyed rising to the challenge.

Since I had a towel by my side and still had a whole pitcher of lemonade left under the table, the solution was obvious. I took two used glasses and washed them off in the pitcher of lemonade, wiped the rims, shook them out and set them back on the table. Horatio Alger would have been proud.

The bus stopped. A skinny guy, looking very hot, got off and put his arms out. "Lemonade, eh?" he said. "Now that will hit the spot. How much?" He flipped two nickels onto the table. "Fill it to the brim, kid."

I took one of the freshly washed glasses and filled it quickly, hoping he wouldn't notice the pieces of lemon clinging to the sides. He picked it up, looked quizzically at the glass for a moment, and said, "Looks a little sticky." But he belted it back like it was a shot glass and let out a real sigh of relief. "You gonna be here tomorrow, kid?"

"Yessir," I replied.

"Good lemonade. But those glasses are really sticky. Where dya wash 'em?"

I thought fast. "I, uh, run down to the Sound and rinse them off there." The man seemed to blanch. "You gotta be kidding? You know what's floating in that water. Jeez, kid, you gotta be out of your mind. I'm gonna report this to someone. Just wait."

Lucky for me a thunderstorm broke the summer's heat that night, and I realized selling lemonade was a risky, seasonal business. So I folded. But for a couple of weeks, I scooted past the corner of Campbell and Agar, hoping the cops wouldn't recognize me.

Anyway, school was starting in a week, and I could hide out there.

AUNTY ROSE'S NOSE.

By Rob Mariani

There is a story my father told at the dinner table one night that amazed me then and has come back to amaze me again and again. Not only was it a very vivid and blood-curdling story, but it revealed a side of my grandfather, Michelangelo Mariani, that I still find hard to reconcile with the man I knew when I was six or seven years old.

To me, grandpa Mariani was always a soft-hearted, cheek-chucking little man with a full head of wiry white hair, a spikey mustache, and a lovingness he could only express with his rough workman's hands and a garbled language of affection—a language that I never really understood because I never heard him speak anything but Italian. And I never saw him wearing anything but a dark gray, three-piece suit, starched white shirt and black tie—even on the hottest summer days in the Bronx, and even when he took my cousin Philip and me fishing on a group charter boat out off Sandy Hook, when his hands became stained with the blood of sandworms and flounders.

My father's description of grandpa as a dad was that of a stern, un-forgiving taskmaster who'd knock you upside the head just for showing up 12 seconds late for lunch. Both his other two children, my Uncle Lou and my Aunty Rose, confirmed this version of their father, but I cannot even recall ever hearing him raise his voice. He just seemed so pleased to have grandchildren that he indulged our every whim and idiosyncrasy. Every Easter, much to my parents' dismay, he'd bring us live pet bunnies or yellow baby chickens in a cardboard box. (Needless to say, none of these poor creatures ever survived for more than a few weeks, but during that time they got lots of petting and unearned attention.)

For years now I've tried to integrate this sweet, loving image of my grandpa with the protagonist in the story of Aunty Rose's nose. She must have been about 12 at the time. Seated at the dinner table with the rest of the family, she was slicing a loaf of Italian bread, bracing the bread against her left thumb as she drew the knife towards her. The bread was perhaps a bit less *al dente* than Aunty rose realized and the knife slipped quickly through the dough and proceeded to slice off the tip of her very prominent, very aquiline, very Italian nose. The large, beak-like Mariani nose is one of the features that clearly identifies my father's side of the family. A trademark, right in the middle of the face that can pass for assertive manliness on a male but is a devastating disfigurement to a female.

As my father recounts what happened next, Rose screamed, blood gushed out onto the tablecloth, and the tip of her nose hung down, swinging by a shred of skin over her lower lip like a piece of bacon.

Grandpa, who believed he could fix anything and usually could, ran to the medicine chest and returned with a band aide which he immediately applied to his daughter's nose, crudely fastening it back onto her face. After a few more strategically placed band aids and some gauze, Rose was laid on her back to stem the blood-flow, and dinner at the Mariani table resumed.

Needless to say, when you do this kind of damage to a nose that was already developing disastrous proportions, the disfigurement grows worse as the nose matures. But doctors were expensive for a family that was barely scraping by on grandpa's meager income, and grandpa's band-aid solution seemed adequate. At least she could breathe, so what else do you want from a nose? Aunty Rose's nose, as grotesque as it became after the accident, wasn't a top family priority. That is until she reached dating age.

As Rose's parents observed the other girls in the neighborhood getting asked out to dances, going steady and then becoming engaged, they realized there was a problem. Rose's nose was not exactly the kind of dowry young men of means were getting down on one knee and begging for. The nose, coupled with the meagerness of the financial package their oldest daughter came with, made Aunty Rose just about un-engageable.

This was in the early 1930's when the terms "plastic surgery" and "nose job" were probably not even in the dictionary. Then a young man named Massimo Quagarelli-- "Moxie" for short-- came along. He was not the most prosperous catch but he had a high school diploma and was heading for a career in the insurance business.

"Mr. Mariani," Moxie said in Italian. "I like your daughter Rose, and I think she would make a good wife. But her nose...."

"What can I do about it? It's the nose she was born with and then she had a little accident."

"Well," said Moxie, "I heard about this doctor. His specialty is fixing messed up noses. A 'plastic surgeon,' they call him. He even did it for some famous movie stars' noses."

When they took Rose to see the doctor, he spoke to them in a very elegant, upper-class Italian dialect that my grandparents could barely understand. The doctor assured them that he had "studied the masters," and could repair Rose's nose perfectly.

He inspired such faith in my grandfather that Michelangelo managed to scrape together just barely enough money for the operation. After a few weeks with dark circles beneath her eyes and breathing through her mouth, Rose was told she could remove the bandages. Her nose was still very sore and very bruised, but even then she could tell that the operation was successful beyond any of the Marianis' wildest dreams. Once the bruises healed, Rose's nose became her most beautiful feature. It was not clipped and upturned or "bobbed' like some pert little June Allison or Doris Day. This was an incredibly graceful, aristocratic and perfectly sculpted nose that gave a whole new meaning to the rest of Rose's face. Suddenly her dark brown eyes seemed to sparkle and her lips and cheekbones took on almost goddess-like proportions. It was clearly the nose Nature had always meant for her to have but that she would never have gotten were it not for that slip of the knife and that spongy loaf of Italian bread.

When Moxie saw her for the first time after the operation, he was so smitten with her beauty that he immediately gave her an engagement ring and set a date for the marriage before the other guys in the neighborhood got a look at the new, improved Rose.

Growing up, Aunty Rose's perfect nose was the only one I ever saw, and I could not imagine what her previous probiscis could possibly have looked like. I was especially perplexed when I compared Aunty Rose's exquisite nose to the rather prominent and forbidding noses the rest of my father's family possessed.

It was not until I was in my mid-thirties and visiting St. Peter's Basilica in Rome for the first time that I realized what it was about Aunty Rose's nose that made it so strikingly beautiful. Because there it was, all around me-- *Aunty Rose's nose*-- on the statues of the angels in the Basilica, on

the peaceful countenances of the virtuous saints in the paint-
ings by Michelangelo and Da Vinci, and even on the gentle,
impeccably pure and beauteous face of the Virgin Mary
herself! Aunty Rose's doctor, obviously a man of genius and
well ahead of his time, had indeed, "studied the masters."

POLIO PIONEER.

By John Mariani

It was not the mushroom cloud image of the A-Bomb I recall with the most horror in the 1950s. The destruction those weapons wrought on Japanese cities brought the end of the long, terrible war, and in an awesome way were images of biblical power and triumph over evil.

Even after the creation of the far more devastating H-bombs and their acquisition by the Soviet Union, which fueled the Cold War and the Red Scare, and even though we went through drills at school in which we hid beneath our desks to protect us from nuclear holocaust, those fiery images seemed distant and impersonal, and we felt protected from them by the promises of our politicians that the Russians risked annihilation (as did we) if such weapons were used. World War III seemed unthinkable, even if those same politicians used the threat of it to build more and more bombs and nuclear submarines.

Far more terrifying to me was a persistent image that seemed very personal indeed, something that could reach into our beds, something for which there was no defense whatsoever. It was the image of the iron lung, a large white barrel of metal in which people—almost all of them children—lay in wait to die from polio.

The "lungs" helped them breathe, but their lives were lived inside of this horrifying machine, and all you could see of them was the children's heads sticking out of a hole in one end. Such images were shown often, as black-and-white photographs in *Life* Magazine, and on T.V. where you could see the children talking, some of them seeming to be in good spirits despite their unthinkable fate.

"That's what happens if you get polio," was the ever-present warning, but it was a warning without hope of prevention. We believed the waters where we swam contained the invisible threat, but it was actually the people who carried it. People we knew and people we didn't know.

There had been an epidemic of the disease in 1916 in which 6,000 Americans died and 27,000 more paralyzed. And in 1952 more than 3,000 had died and more than 20,000 had been paralyzed.

President Roosevelt, it was later revealed, lived his life as a polio victim, though he never suffered the fate of the iron lung. We always saw him seated in photos and newsreels, his frailty hidden from us, his polio a terrible secret. Everyone knew someone who had a polio victim in their family, and they were spoken of in whispers, until their limbs became useless and they could not breathe and had to be inserted into the iron lung until their wasted bodies gave up, sometimes after years in the iron lung. And most died, without ever having any hope of real recovery.

Then, in 1954, Dr. Jonas Salk created a vaccine he truly believed could prevent polio. But to prove that it could he needed a vast number of children on which to test it out—an idea that would require an unprecedented national volunteer program of surrendering one's children to the possibility that the vaccine might actually cause polio to develop.

The crusade was, however, promoted with remarkable

restraint and sensitivity, and for once the politicians stayed mostly clear of the stage that was set by the American medical community. The stakes were very high that this vaccine could be a way to wipe out the disease, while the stakes that a child would contract polio from it were said to be small. But to give up your child for a medical experiment?

Children started to hear about the plan from whispers in the house and news reports, but we knew nothing about it until everything was ready to bring thousands of children in to get a shot.

I was nine years old when the experiment was to begin, and I was told about it by my teacher, who gave us sealed envelopes to take home to our parents. The secretive nature of what was about to happen made the mystery of it all that scarier, and the fact that there was a needle involved made the prospects grim.

I brought the envelope home and gave it to my mother, who opened it, read it with a strange mixture of concern and hopefulness on her face. "What is it?" I asked.

"Oh, let's wait till Dad gets home, then we'll talk about it." If ever there was a phrase to put an eight year-old into trepidation, that was it. My mind raced and my thoughts were occupied by nothing else but the contents of that envelope. Our teacher only told us that we might be "pioneers for science," which could have been anything from taking intelligence tests to joining the first rocket flight into space.

My father came home as usual at seven o'clock, and he and my mother spoke quietly about the envelope as he took his tie and shirt off in the bedroom. "I'd like to see him do it," said my father. "I think this is very important."

"But it could be dangerous, Al," said Renee. "Didn't they say it could actually cause him to come down with polio?"

This was getting personal, and I felt a shiver shoot down my spine as my mind conjured up a black-and-white image of my head sticking out of an iron lung. At 13 Robert was too old for the experiment, but I was of prime age. They were going to round up all us little kids and shoot us with a needle and it might make us get polio and end up in the iron lung!

After a long, curiously quiet dinner, my father began.

"Listen, John, I want to talk to you about something very serious, something that could be very wonderful for all children."

I was riveted to my chair, my eyes wide.

"I know you know what polio is, John, and know you've seen those pictures of those poor kids in the iron lungs. And now a doctor has invented this thing called a vaccine—it's kind of a medicine—that might stop kids from ever getting polio. And the doctors want to do an experiment to try this medicine out to prove it will work. They want to give kids a little shot, like the ones you got when you were a little guy that left you with that little spot on your arm, right there."

He pointed at the vaccination mark on my left arm, and I flinched back.

"I don't want to get a shot! They hurt!"

"John, try to understand how important this is, how you would be like a hero if you got this shot and it worked."

"You mean it might *not* work?"

"Well, these doctors are very confident it will."

"But what if it doesn't? Will I get polio?"

I saw my mother out of the corner of my eye with her fist to her mouth.

"That's very very very unlikely," Al said softly, shaking his head.

"But I could, couldn't I?" By now I was getting visibly upset, insisting that I not get the shot.

My father stopped talking and nodded. "O.K., but let me fill out the forms telling them you don't want to get the shot."

There was no relief for me in hearing this, for I had a strong sense of betraying my father's sense of trust in me. I knew I was acting like a baby, but even in my eight year-old mind, swirling with thoughts of the iron lung, I could not bring myself to accede to my father's wishes.

The next morning I came to breakfast and saw the envelope lying on the kitchen table. My mother was cooking breakfast and my father was still getting dressed. I touched the envelope. Then I picked it up and took out the sheets of paper. There, in my father's handwriting, were answers to questions about me, my name, age, school, and what sicknesses I'd had as a child. Then, where there were two boxes, there was a check mark in one that read "I agree to allow my child to take part in this experiment," followed by many, many words I did not understand. I was on the verge of panic when my father entered the room.

"You said I didn't have to get the shot," I screamed. "You lied to me! You said I didn't have to get the shot."

Renee came over and put her arms on my shoulders as I started to cry.

My father, more sad than shaken, put out his hands to calm me. "I know, I did say that, but, John, this is just so important. It's for you and all the other kids' future. Please say you'll do it."

But by then I was crying deeply, and I watched my father scratch out the box and check off the other that said I would not participate in the experiment. "All right," he said. "You don't have to take the shot. Just think about it when you get to school, and give them back this envelope."

My brother, having witnessed most of this scene, proceeded to make fun of me, that I was a little creep and a sissy, but my father silently admonished him with the lifting of one hand. The ride to school was in silence.

When I got to school I saw that some of my classmates had already handed in their envelopes, which were in two piles—the ones from kids who were volunteering, the rest, a smaller pile, from kids who were not. I hesitated taking mine out of my book bag, and then Brother Clarke asked me for my envelope. "What are you going to do, John?" He asked. "Will you volunteer for this experiment or not?" I held the envelope in my hand, the paper moist from my sweat. I looked again at the piles.

"Well, I, I was not going to do it, Brother, but, I, well, I think maybe I will."

"Good boy, John. Your father and mother will be proud of you."

He looked at the papers, noted that there was a discrepancy in the checked boxes, and said, "Let me give you another envelope. Your dad can fill it out again and you can bring it back tomorrow."

It was not long after that when the great experiment took place in schools and hospitals all over America. Those at our school who participated were taken by bus to a local public school where, with dozens of children we didn't know, we were inoculated, half with the vaccine, half with water. As I came closer on the line to receiving my shot, I watched little girls taking it without so much as a wince, while some boys broke into tears even before the needle touched them.

A nurse pulled up my sleeve, quickly wiped it with a cold wet cotton ball, then held the syringe up to the light and squirted a little into the air. "This is only going to hurt a little teeny bit," she smiled, and as I closed my eyes, she poked the needle into my arm. "All over," she said, wiping my arm again and applying a clean Band-Aid. "You were very brave, and you did a very brave thing."

I went back to school and, for the most part, forgot about what happened, except to tell my parents with pride that I didn't cry and that the nurse said I was brave, and that all the kids got cards with our names written on them in blue ink, reading "POLIO PIONEER."

That day more than half a million American children were inoculated, 444,000 with the vaccine, 210,000 with water.

Soon afterwards, they published in the newspapers lists of all the children who participated in the experiment, curiously separating those who received the vaccine and those who received the water, which had the effect of bringing the threat of contracting polio back into my mind along with the iron lung pictures. Yet my pride in being a Polio Pioneer far outweighed all thoughts of the disease, and I was very happy that I had gotten the vaccine, not the water—a published, verifiable fact I paraded before my classmates the next day.

Then we all held our breath for the rest of the year.

Months went by, and finally, on April 12, 1955, the news broke: In an auditorium at the University of Michigan Dr. Thomas Francis, a mentor of Dr. Salk, pronounced that the vaccine was a complete success, measured by the fact that the vaccinated children—including me—did not contract polio that or any other year, while some of those who got the water did. That this announcement was made amid what the *New York Times* called "fanfare and drama far more typical of a Hollywood premiere than a medical meeting" did nothing to detract from the earthshaking news. Twenty-seven million doses had already been stockpiled for release, and the next day children began to get shots that would effectively wipe out the dreaded disease. A wave of anxiety arose just one month later when it was found one manufacturer had not properly killed the viruses in its vaccine, and of the thousands who received those batches, 260 developed polio.

But the horror of that incident was quickly forgotten in the wake of the vaccine's success, and soon all American children were vaccinated quickly and then the vaccine spread throughout the world, added to by an oral vaccine developed by Dr. Albert Sabin.Within years all children were being vaccinated against the horrible scourge. Dr. Jonas Salk won the Nobel Prize in Medicine for his work that seemed almost a miracle. In 2004 there were only 1,263 cases of polio discovered in the entire world.

I still have and am equally proud of my Polio Pioneer card, which I keep in my night table drawer. From the day the news came that the vaccine had worked, the images of the children in the iron lungs faded too, relics of a sad and hopeless era I and thousands of other little boys and girls had completely eradicated in the year 1954.

PINK BELLY.

By John Mariani

I can't say my brother Robert and I ever really got along as kids. He was five years older than I was and when I was really little he regarded me at best as a noisome nuisance. This turned at times into real taunts and wrestling matches I could never win as I entered grammar school and succeeded beyond my parents' expectation as Robert's school career foundered year after year. Many times I'd bring back a report card with all A's on it, but my parents' pride and praise paled behind the frustrations they felt when Robert handed in his own deficient report card. They'd spend the whole night berating him, asking him why, *how* he could do so poorly because he was such a smart kid and then *this*, C-, C-, D+, C, C+.

Yet my admiration for my brother, even when he was being reckless, was very strong and very abiding. I looked up to him for his ingenuous charm, his good, blue-eyed looks—he'd even posed for the cover of a magazine once, in a tweed cap, holding a ruler in his hands. I had dark eyes, dark hair, and was always just a little chubby—I wore a children's size then called "Husky"—and I never thought of myself as attractive except to endless Italian relatives who used to pinch my cheeks and my legs.

Robert and I didn't really have much to do with one another. I never recall talking to him in our beds—the headboard of his up against the headboard of mine. We had different interests simply because of our ages, though both of us shared an intense interest in the same T.V. shows and comic books, which ranged from Donald Duck to Captain Marvel, and even though I was only six or seven, the appearance of a new issue of the amazingly irreverent, pungently satirical *MAD* comics (it later became a magazine) was greeted by both of us with a kind of devilish glee.

But Robert's friends would never be mine, and I was usually the object of their jokes.

Then one day while walking up Campbell Drive towards the Club, I saw one of the new kids in the neighborhood who had not yet been embraced by the cliques of other boys in the neighborhood. My brother only knew him a little bit, and I'd never seen him at our house. His name was Mike Dunn, a fat Irish kid with the requisite red hair, always dirty, and freckles scattered on sweaty pinkish skin.

I was with Johnny Flaherty, who was my age and height; Mike Dunn was with another kid his age whom I had never seen. As we approached them I started to get the animal-like feeling that I was in potential trouble. They waited for us to get to the end of the block, then Mike spoke.

"Hey, you little punk, where you going?"

I kept walking. "To the Club."

"Oh yeah? I don't think so. I think you should lie on the ground and lemme give you a pink belly!"

I had only heard about getting a pink belly, and, frankly, was surprised Robert had never doled one out to me. All I knew was that I was about to get sat on and have my stomach slapped till it turned pink. Dunn grabbed me by one arm and forced me down to the ground. Johnny Flaherty told him to stop but the other kid pushed up against him and said, "Shut up and keep out of it!"

The bestial, piggy-looking Mike Dunn was now sitting on my legs. "Jimmy, hold his arms down!" Jimmy knelt and pinned my arms. Johnny Flaherty ran across the street and yelled, "I'm telling my mother!" By then Mike had my t-shirt up and over my head, and my ordeal began. He started slapping my stomach, first one slap, then a second, then he built it up into a rhythm as I tried to squirm free. He kept it up until I heard the brogue voice of Johnny Flaherty's mother, "What are you doin' to that poor child? Let 'im up this second or I'll smack you blind!"

By the time Mrs. Flaherty was halfway across the street, Mike Dunn and Jimmy were off me and running down the street, laughing like hyenas, shaking their heads, then looking back at Mrs. Flaherty and sticking out their tongues at her. I pulled the shirt off my head and Mrs. Flaherty helped me up. I looked down at my stomach and it was as pink as a pig and still stung. "Lemme look at you," Mrs. Flaherty said. "Oh, John, I think you'll live. Nothin' but a bit o' pink."

I was crying and pulled myself away from her and ran home, rushing into my bedroom and pushing my head into the pillow. My brother was in the room and asked, "What happened to you, stupid?" I told him the story and how Mike Dunn ran away. Robert shrugged and said, "Ah, you're OK. Mike's a moron."

I hadn't expected much sympathy from my brother and got none. I stopped crying just to spite him.

But the next day I was astonished to hear Mike Dunn's voice in my living room, along with Robert's and Richie Swift's. I started to perspire and my anger at Robert's allowing this wretched swine into our house after what he'd done to me the day before caused me to run in and shout, "Get outta my house, you stinking creep!" Robert put his hands up and said, "Hey, calm down, you jerk. I'm just showing Mike how to use my air rifle." This, the same air rifle I was not allowed even to get near to! And then I saw something I would never have thought possible.

Robert, with Richie's urging, told Mike to cock the rifle but not to push the cocking handle back into the stock. "Why not?" the pig asked.

Robert shook his head. "Don't you know you get more power if you *don't* put the handle back in?"

"Really?" said Mike, letting the handle hang free.

"Now aim and feel how it kicks."

There was no BB in the gun so Mike raised it to his shoulder, squinted carefully through the metal sight, and slowly pulled the trigger. The rifle went off with a *p-chung!* in the same split second the handle snapped back onto Mike's beefy, thick fingers. I thought I heard a crack of bones. Mike let out a scream of agony but he was too shocked to pull the handle back. "Get it off! Get it off!" he screeched, slobbering and squealing. Richie grabbed the rifle and pried back the handle. Mike's three last fingers were gashed and bleeding, deep gashes. He howled some more while Robert and Richie just laughed their asses off. I was in a state of shock, my mouth gaping open at both the surprise of the moment and the outright viciousness of my brother's ensnarement.

"That'll teach you to give my brother a pink belly, you little shit. Now get the hell out of my house, and if we see you on the block again, me and my friends will give you more than a stinking pink belly."

I stood there in amazement, thrilled by what I'd seen, fascinated by the exquisite meanness and the brutal inventiveness of my brother's revenge plot. I looked at him and said, "Robbie, I can't believe you did that." Richie Swift was still laughing.

"Yea, well, just make sure you never touch my air rifle, you understand? Get lost, creep."

My brother has always told me he doesn't remember that story at all. But I'll never forget it.

UNCLE MATTY VS.THE LITTLE GENERAL.

By Rob Mariani

I never really knew if he was a friend of the family because he was our doctor or if he was our doctor because he was a friend of the family. But Dr. Matt Coppola was the one we all went to for everything from shots and poison ivy to allergies and tonsillitis. And I'm sure if we'd needed brain surgery, we'd have gone to him for that, too. He took very literally the term "General Practitioner" and would tackle just about any medical problem you threw his way.

"Uncle Matty," as we called him had an office in a gritty neighborhood just off Gunhill Road. When we were there, we always called him "Doctor Coppola." On social occasions, we called him Uncle Matty because "Uncle" is what we called any of our family's close male friends.

Uncle Matty was so successful as a doctor that by the time he was 40 years old, he was well on his way to acquiring a very large portion of the American Dream as it was envisioned there in the beginning of the 1950's. He had a big three-story house in the lovely Pelham Gardens neighborhood. His neighbors were other doctors, lawyers, professional people, and the championship boxer, Jake LaMotta, "The

Bronx Bull." Matty's son Donny and his daughter Marjorie both attended exclusive private Catholic schools. He had a big maroon Cadillac with the push-up bra headlights and fish tail taillights. He had a beautiful little summer house across the sound in Stony Brook, Long Island. It overlooked the lagoon of the yacht club. So, naturally, to complete the picture he bought a yacht.

It was really just a small in-board motorboat with a cabin. There was no room for a head or a galley. It had a couple of padded benches in the bow where two people could sleep uncomfortably. The only thing Matty knew about boats was that he liked them. A lot. He spent every summer weekend he could on his boat, which he enigmatically named "The Little General."

"Why not 'The Little *Admiral*'?" my father would ask him.

"Sounds too 'nautical'," was his reply.

Uncle Matty got himself a white captain's hat and a berth at one of the many shipyards on City Island, just a five-minute drive from his house. He joined the yacht club in Stony Brook. He learned the difference between starboard and port and was ready to take on the challenge of the sea.

I think the first boat lasted one season. Uncle Matty would invite our family of four to join his family and we'd chug out to the edge of Pelham Bay where we kids could fish and the adults could have Tom Collinses. But Uncle Matty soon felt the need for a larger vessel. And evidently he had the means to buy one because the next season, "The Little General II" was in Uncle Matty's slip at the boatyard.

The Little General II was nearly three times the size of his original craft. It was a real yacht with a flying bridge, sleeping accommodations for five or six, an actual galley, and a toilet and shower, an indoor "lounge," and a fantail spacious enough to accommodate eight martini-drinkers on deckchairs. Now Uncle Matty had a boat that was seaworthy enough to go from City Island in the Bronx up Pelham Bay and across the Long Island Sound to his summer home in Stony Brook. He was in heaven.

On a typical sunny Saturday in June, my father and mother and brother and I would all arrive at the dock before noon and pile on board. Uncle Matty would be there, already having downed a couple of eye-openers—Bloody Marys, usually. He was dressed in his captain's hat, tan bathing trunks and a Hawaiian sport shirt, unbuttoned all the way down the front to reveal a very unpleasant surgical scar. He'd had his gallbladder removed a few years ago and from the look of the scar, I used to think maybe he'd done the job himself. Uncle Matty was a slim, bony man with a dark Mediterranean complexion and a pencil-thin mustache. He breathed through his nose when he talked and his tone of voice always implied a kind of reassuring "it's-ok-it's-gonna-be-awright" attitude.

His wife Dot was a beautiful, blue-eyed Irish brunette who made lasagna that caused many of her Italian friends to shake their heads in admiration. She could even make it in "The Little General's" limited galley space. Uncle Matty's intrepid seafaring adventures made her nervous, but she went along for the ride and to make sure he didn't drown the kids. In the afternoon she'd pop two or three aspirin and a Coke to calm herself down.

With Uncle Matty at the helm, by one P.M. we'd have steamed out of Pelham Bay and were out on Long Island Sound with land a distant smudge on the horizon. One of the big thrills was seeing herds of porpoises frolicking in our wake. Sometimes they'd follow us for hours. Up on the flying bridge, Uncle Matty would let us kids take turns steering and it would start to feel like a pretty thrilling adventure, like something out of the Saturday morning movie serial, *Don Winslow of the U.S. Navy.*

There'd be lunch down in the lounge or out on the fan-tail. Aunt Dot's lasagna, or hero sandwiches with prosciutto and mozzarella. The dads drank from copper-colored cans of Ballantine beer and the moms all had their silvery Tom Collinses. Earlier in the voyage, Uncle Matty would partake of what he embarrassingly referred to as his "coffee enema." This meant that at precisely 3pm, regardless of where we were or what else was going on, he'd stop the boat, drop anchor, light up a Chesterfield, and spend a good half-hour in the head. We kids would use this time to porpoise-watch or fish. Sometimes we'd catch a few flounders and eels, but mostly we'd hook sea robins, a very inedible, prehistoric-looking creature that could put up a good fight.

The commute by boat from City Island to Uncle Matty's summer place in Stony Brook, even with "The Little General's" supercharged engines, was a good seven hours. Towards the end of the summer, as the days grew shorter, instead of making the long haul, Uncle Matty would stay closer to home, cruising along the coast and finding a water-side restaurant where we'd tie up at the dock and have dinner.

Dinner with Uncle Matty was a kind of culinary opera with large, bravura arias of food separated by long, drawn out recitatives filled with martinis and Chianti. This one particular night Uncle Matty started out with a bucket of steamers followed by three or four cigarettes and a brace of dry martinis. Then came the lobster and steak washed down with wine and beer, another round of nicotine, some espresso and cheese cake followed by a few brandies.

By the time the meal was over, it was pitch dark outside and the grownups, including Uncle Matty, were three-sheets-to-the-wind, to put it nautically. Now it was up to our woozy captain to get us back across the Bay to City Island. The trip was probably only about three or four miles as the gull flies, but Uncle Matty, not the most accomplished seaman to begin with, was having trouble just finding his way back to the boat. Dot, the dutiful wife, had kept her drinking moderate and was able to guide her staggering husband to "The Little

General." Once on board, miraculously, Matty somehow clambered his way up to the flying bridge. My dad and I went with him. He started the engines and slipped into reverse, plowing the stern of the boat right into the pier. Dishes and glasses in the downstairs lounge slid to the floor and broke. The ladies laughed nervously. Dot rolled her blue eyes.

"It's-ok-it's-gonna-be-awright, Dotty," Uncle Matty called out through his nose and promptly flipped the boat into forward gear. With a lurch we came away from the dock at full throttle and were almost instantly traveling at about 30 knots creating waves which nearly swamped the buoy with the sign that read: "No Wakes."

The seas were calm that night and a big full moon had just come up over the horizon. Uncle Matty aimed the boat at the moon. Beneath it were the little blinking lights of the shoreline which we all hoped was our City Island destination. As we got out into open waters the waves began to swell gently beneath "The Little General's" hull and we took on a forward undulating motion.

Squinting into the darkness, Uncle Matty located the red blinking buoy and the green blinking buoy and was endeavoring to set a course between the two to avoid going aground.

After about 20 minutes, the boat's engines gave a kind of surging, sputtering noise and then promptly quit. Uncle Matty turned the ignition key several times but all this produced was a strained, raspy sound, like someone coughing up sea water. Our captain had done a flawless job of refueling himself at our waterside landing but had evidently neglected to do the same for "The Little General." Two miles out into the Bay, nine o'clock at night, and there we all were, adrift in the moonlight, out of gas. In the distance, we could hear what sounded like a foghorn although, as I said, the night was clear.

Uncle Matty went below to the ship-to-shore radio and after reading the instruction manual by flashlight, he managed to call the Coast Guard for help. He continued to reassure us in his "it's-awright-don't-worry-about-it" tone of voice, as if we were one of his patients about to undergo a fairly if-y operation. We sat there on the flying bridge, Uncle Matty, my father, and I, and watched for the Coast Guard cutter. The sound of the rolling waters became fuller and now there was a low vibration in the soft, warm air. The vibration seemed to be emanating up from the water. It was getting louder and then all at once the moon disappeared from the sky.

"Must be clouds passing over," Uncle Matty said to my father, his speech calm and more than a little slurred from booze. But as we stared into the sudden darkness, a huge rust-colored wall was taking shape directly in front of us. It blocked out the entire sky. We began to hear the sound of waves crashing rhythmically against hollow steel. Then the foghorn sound, which had seemed miles away just a few minutes before, exploded off the bow of the boat like some yawning volcano. We realized that we were in the direct path of a huge freighter as it headed full-speed-ahead out of the Bay. The ear-shattering foghorn sounded again. Uncle Matty cranked the ignition and pumped his own ship's shrill horn and began frantically flicking his running lights. The hull of the freighter towered over us now. We leaned back in our chairs and gripped the railings preparing to be run over. From down in the lounge, we heard a woman's scream. There was a slight bump as the bow of "The Little General" glanced lightly off the side of the freighter. We felt ourselves being turned and lifted in the behemoth's wake. By some miracle, "The Little General" had just missed being cut in half and instead had been nudged gently aside by the freighter. We bobbed now in the rolling wake.

"Everybody ok down there?" my dad called off the side of the flying bridge. "Yes, we're all right," came Dot's high voice through the half-open window. It sounded a bit like a sob.

I looked over at Uncle Matty where he stood by the steering wheel of his lifeless boat. He pushed his captain's hat to the back of his head and scratched his thinning hair. He stared into the darkness after the retreating freighter, then lit up a Chesterfield and exhaled the smoke into the night. He offered one to my dad who had recently been trying to quit smoking and he accepted it without hesitation.

The silence was broken by the sound of the Coast Guard cutter's horn. They towed us in to port and helped secure the boat to the dock. Nobody said much. We all went to our respective cars. Dot helped her husband into the passenger seat of their Caddy. Donny and Margery piled into the back seat. Dot got behind the wheel and they pulled away.

A couple of summers went by and Uncle Matty continued to prosper. He bought himself an even larger boat and christened it "The Donny-Mar," in honor of his kids who by now preferred leprosy to spending another moment on the water with their old man.

This time, Uncle Matty had the good sense to hire a mate to pilot his boat. He was a handsome young 19-year-old Spanish kid everyone called "Sunshine" because he had a smile that could light up a ballroom. From then on, it was pretty clear sailing for Uncle Matty. Sunshine knew everything there was to know about boating and engines and safety on the water. Uncle Matty still steered his boat in open water where he couldn't get into any trouble, at least until cocktail hour when Sunshine would take over.

The only drawback to Uncle Matty's hiring Sunshine was that his teenage daughter Marjorie fell in love with him. But that's another story.

A SMALL EPIDEMIC.

By Rob Mariani

My mother explained to me that they were orphans. Like the little girl in the Sunday comic strip with the red hair and the brown dog. They were kids just like us, only they didn't have any parents. Didn't have them, or had been "given up" by them, as our parents pointed out whenever they wanted to remind us that we were privileged.

There were six orphans on the ground floor of the two-family Rawlins house just down the street from us on Campbell Drive. Four girls and two boys. They ranged in age from about five or six to fourteen or fifteen. They lived like brothers and sisters but they didn't look alike and they weren't really related. They lived in a "foster home" with "foster parents," people who took them in and agreed to raise them... for money. The name of the foster parents was Rawlins and everyone referred to them as "The Rawlins kids," but the kids themselves didn't use that last name. They never used any last name that I can recall.

Both the foster boys were named Joe. They were about the same age, 10 years old, but one was taller and so they became "Big Joe" and "Little Joe." Big Joe wore his hair short like a Marine and he could whack a baseball farther than anybody else in the neighborhood, but he hardly ever wanted to play with us. He always seemed to have someplace else to go, out of the neighborhood. He was the first kid to start smoking cigarettes. Of all the orphan kids, Big Joe was the one who seemed the angriest.

Little Joe looked very Aryan, with white-blond hair, sharp Germanic features and clear blue eyes. I remember seeing a Pathé Newsreel of "Hitler's Youth" and there was a kid in it who looked just like Little Joe with those staring eyes. But Little Joe was frail and acted afraid all the time, as if he were going to be punished for something he hadn't even done yet. And the more Little Joe acted afraid, the more we non-orphan kids in the neighborhood would pick on him. Richie Swift stole his little blue cap and threw it up into one of the chestnut trees behind the wall at the Villa Maria Academy.

Alice was Little Joe's foster sister. She had long blond braids and green eyes and was going to grow up to be movie-star-gorgeous. She also had a temper and she liked to yell at the other orphan kids and boss them around. When she got mad, her voice became very loud and impossible to ignore. Naturally, she was the one we liked to tease most.

And there was Rue-Rue, who was the same age as Alice, also about ten. She had big dark eyes and black hair and very red cheeks as if someone had been pinching them, and her nose ran a lot, regardless of whether it was summer or winter. Rue-Rue talked in a high screechy baby voice even when everything was calm and there was no need for it, which made it hard to be around her. You got the feeling she didn't really want to be near anyone most of the time anyway.

She liked to sing corny old radio commercials to herself, like the Tom Mix Hot Ralston song or the Ajax Cleanser jingle, but she'd change the words and sometimes even make up words that sounded like they were another language— Commanche or Egyptian maybe.

Sometimes when you talked to Rue-Rue she would seem to lose track of the conversation and her gaze would go off somewhere over your shoulder and not come back and you'd lose her.

There was also Baby Dolores, who was about four. She had big long eyelashes and skin a shade darker than anyone else's in the neighborhood.

The house the orphans lived in was the shabbiest two-family house in a neighborhood that was trying to move upward. The dark green paint on the front of the house was peeling and there were holes in the screens and bleak white window shades instead of curtains in the windows. On nights when the shades were not pulled down all the way, you could see into the front room where all the kids slept and there was just a plain naked light bulb overhead and cracks in the plaster walls.

One winter the orphan kids all came down with whooping cough. Our parents warned us to stay away from them, not even to set foot on their driveway, because it was a very contagious disease and kids could die from it. Passing by the orphans' house to get to my grandmother's one night as the first snowflakes of winter began to fall, I heard them in the front room whooping and coughing. It sounded like a cage of coyotes or wild dogs. One of the front windows was open a crack and I stopped to listen. I couldn't see in but I was able to distinguish one kid's whoop-and-cough from another's. Big Joe's cough sounded like air being squeezed from a bellows. And Little Joe sounded like a puppy who'd had its tail stepped on.

The girls each had their own wheezing cough too. Rue-Rue's was especially upsetting because it was the highest pitched and I could picture her red cheeks and runny nose with the green snot running down her upper lip.

I covered my mouth and nose with my mitten and ran past the Rawlins' house to the safety of my grandmother's about three houses down.

None of the other kids in the neighborhood caught the Whooping Cough that year because our parents took us to be vaccinated against it. Still we were warned that the little circle Uncle Matty etched on our upper arm was not foolproof. For weeks, every time I passed by the crumbling old worn down Rawlins house, I could hear the orphan kids inside whooping and wheezing. I remember thinking how unfair it seemed, as if being orphans was not hard enough, they had to get whooping cough too. And I felt guilty for the times we had all ganged up on Little Joe, and for the time we'd made him eat an ice ball, and the time we'd tried to smother him in a cardboard box.

We stole Alice's navy blue stocking cap once too and threw it up into a tree. When she climbed up to get it, we looked up under her skirt and saw her faded gray underpants. I even felt guilty for teasing Rue-Rue about her chapped red cheeks and calling her "bird face," which was what everybody called her from then on.

It was an unusually warm, windless day in February when the orphan kids finally came back out on the street again. I was throwing my pink Spaldine against my grandmother's stoop, practicing for the upcoming stoop ball season. I looked up and saw Big Joe come out of the house first. He lit a cigarette, hawked up a loogie and spit it into the scruffy hedges. Then shoving his hands into his jacket pockets, he strode off and disappeared around the corner up Polo Place, the cigarette smoke trailing after him like a ghost.

Little Joe, Alice and Dolores came out onto the dilapidated front steps next. They looked very pale and timid, like a small herd of deer stepping out onto a frozen lake. I kept on punching the ball against the steps. I'd almost gotten used to the orphans not being around.

Alice had her own pink Spaldine. She came slowly

down the sidewalk towards me bouncing it and throwing her leg over it saying the "A-my-name-is-Alice" chant as she approached. By the time she got near me, she was up to "L-my-name-is-Linda-and-I-come-from-London...."

Alice looked pale and her face was thinner. There were slight indentations on both cheeks and her hair was lank and dull. She spoke in a low, raspy whisper which made her sound like she had gravel in her throat.

"Hi," she said and stopped bouncing her ball.

"You had the whooping cough, huh." I said.

She bounced the ball once and swung her leg over it and there was the slightest glimpse of her faded gray-blue underpants again. "Yeah, so what? We all had it," Alice said, kneeling down on the sidewalk. She took a piece of yellow chalk out of her pocket and started to draw lines on the concrete.

"Rue-Rue's gone," she said very quietly after a few minutes, not looking up at me. "They took her to the hospital 'cause she couldn't breathe."

"When's she coming back?" I asked, tossing my ball straight up over my head and catching it softly underhanded.

Alice shook her head and kept staring down at what she was drawing. "Ma Rawlins said Rue-Rue's not."

"Not what?"

"Not coming back."

I bounced the ball hard on the ground once right next to her, showing off, but when it came back down Alice grabbed it and folded it in behind her arms with her own ball.

"Hey, gimme my ball."

Alice shook her head and clutched it closer. She leaned back on her heels and her little black wool skirt fell away from her legs almost revealing her underpants again.

"I see London, I see France, I see Alice's underpants!" I screamed.

Alice stood up fast and flung the ball at my head. I got my hands up just in time to catch it. I saw right away that it wasn't my ball. Little Rue-Rue's name was hand-printed on it in black ink. Instinctively I flung the ball right back at Alice as if it were a hot rivet. It hit her in the shoulder as she turned to run away. The pink rubber ball rolled around on the sidewalk where Alice had been drawing with her chalk. I gave the ball a kick with the toe of my shoe that sent it skipping across the street and it disappeared into the oblong slot on the curb where the rainwater drained into the sewer.

THE PILGRIM.

By John Mariani

It was clear to just about everybody in 1953 that going to the movies was soon to be a thing of the past, like going to World's Fairs. Television had changed everything, and now that you could actually see good Hollywood movies on T.V. ("MIllion Dollar Movie" had the best ones, shown twice a night for an entire week), it had to be something really special to draw you out of the house to go to a movie theater.

The only thing the movies still had going for them was Technicolor, which reached a high art in the early fifties, and the fact that there were still some things they couldn't show on television. Actually, there was a whole lot they couldn't show on television, like married people in the same bed.

The Catholic Church was as zealous as the anti-communist crusaders in finding filth and immorality in every movie frame, and its proscriptive arm was called the Legion of Decency, which rated movies according to their sinfulness and fitness for people to see, awarding a dreaded "C" for "Condemned" to movies completely beyond the bounds of human decency, movies sprung from demented imaginations and the devil's own workshop, which was apparently set up in the soundstages of Paramount, RKO, Columbia and Universal. A "C"-rated picture meant not only that Catholics were forbidden to go see it but that any who did would be committing a mortal sin and be condemned to hell if they died on the way back from the movie theater.

The list of condemned movies was usually reserved for torrid, grainy European entries, but a mild romantic Hollywood farce called "The Moon Is Blue" got slapped with a scarlet "C" simply because William Holden used the word "virgin" in the third reel. It was the biggest scandal since Clark Gable said "Frankly, my dear, I don't give a damn" in "Gone with the Wind." Neither word was something you were ever going to hear on TV shows like "My Little Margie."

Far more deserving of condemnation was a Technicolor bible epic in the long line of golden calf potboilers Hollywood had tricked up since the silent era, always filled with plenty of murders, drunkenness and all-out orgies. This latest blasphemy was entitled "Salome," which starred Stewart Granger, Charles Laughton, Cedric Hardwicke, Judith Anderson and Rita Hayworth as the title character whose furious striptease they called the "Dance of the Seven Veils" was considered so egregiously erotic as to earn this Hollywood movie the scarlet "C."

As kids, we thought being a reviewer for the Legion of Decency would be the greatest job in the world: You'd get to sit in the movies all day watching to see if people said "virgin" while women like Rita Hayworth took their veils off.

You'd sit there counting up the number of times people cursed and probably had to ask the projectionist to run a scene back and forth a few times to make sure a nipple or something worse wasn't exposed for so much as a frame.

Movies still had some pull, but by 1952 attendance had dropped to two-thirds what it had been in 1946, and Hollywood was reduced to turning out only about half the pictures they had before the war. In 1949 the Supreme Court drove the studios out of theater ownership, a monopolistic practice that guaranteed their best and worst movies would be shown while the studios collected the lion's share of the profits. After that decision came down, theater owners no longer had to screen whatever junk the studios sent them, so Hollywood stopped making a lot of risky pictures, serials, cartoons and "B" movies.

Hollywood had also been riven by the anti-Communist hysteria of the late Forties. Led by the House Un-American Activities Committee and encouraged by scared-stiff studio heads who caved in under pressure and gave names of suspected commie sympathizers in their midst, a notorious "blacklist" was drawn up of more than 200 filmmakers and actors, many of whom disappeared from the screen for more than a decade.

So, to get us away from our T.V. sets and into the theater seats, Hollywood had to come up with new gimmicks we couldn't see at home. The first was Cinerama in 1952--an image projected on three curved screens spread out along a gigantic stage so that it matched the entire range of the human eye and "put the audience in the picture." But the process was very costly and did not lend itself to widespread exhibition, so a year later Hollywood came up with simpler wide-screen options called Cinemascope, VistaVision, Cinemiracle and Todd-AO, which were easily adapted to most movie theaters.

Hollywood also tackled themes and subject matter you couldn't see at home--deranged sexuality in Tennessee Williams' "A Streetcar Named Desire," corrupt labor unions in "On the Waterfront," military cowardice in "The Red Badge of Courage," the curdled American Dream in "Death of a Salesman," western anti-heroes in "Shane" and "High Noon," even motorcycle gangs in "The Wild One."

There were new, provocative stars like Marilyn Monroe, Marlon Brando, Montgomery Clift, Burt Lancaster, Kirk

Douglas, Judy Holliday and Patricia Neal, whose neurotic behavior and sweaty demeanors bore little resemblance to the clean image of stars of Hollywood's Golden Age.

What really pulled us into the theaters, though, was rank spectacle, movies like "King Solomon's Mines," "Samson and Delilah," "The Robe," "Quo Vadis," and "The Greatest Show on Earth," masterpieces of high kitsch and low morals.

But beyond all these, there was what Hollywood was calling "The Next Big Thing" in 1953: 3-D movies. This you could not get at home.

The Bronx had some incredible movie theaters, foremost among them the Loew's Paradise on the Grand Concourse and 188th Street-- a 4,000 seat auditorium with a night sky painted on the ceiling and enough gilt, statuary, birds of paradise, and marble fountains to serve as the setting for a Cecil B. DeMille bacchanal. It was the most glamorous thing in the entire Bronx, better than Radio City. It was dreamy.

Here some of the biggest first-run movies debuted, and even though such movies usually only played for about a week at the Paradise, people drove from all over to catch it before it moved on to smaller theaters around the Bronx. A debut at the Paradise was quite an event.

Most theaters were more modest, though most had a certain grandeur and a size that made the single showing of a double feature consistently profitable for the new independent theater owner. There was a drive-in over near the Whitestone Bridge that was particularly popular with teenagers, and on moonlit nights there was no more romantic or terrifying place to be, depending on whether the picture starred Ava Gardner or Vincent Price.

The great thing about the drive-in was that you could yell, scream, laugh your head off, make wisecracks at the actors and do a lot of other things impossible to get away with in a regular theater like the Interboro on Tremont

Avenue, which had earned the undying nickname "The Itch," because it had apparently been infested with fleas a decade before. Or you could make out for ninety minutes.

But our neighborhood theater was the Pilgrim. It was big, had a sizeable balcony, and you could get an extra jolt of excitement if the elevated subway outside rattled the place at just the right dramatic moment, like when the jungle drums started up in "King Solomon's Mines" or Victor Mature toppled the pagan temple in "Samson and Delilah."

The Pilgrim was known for its Saturday all-day children's programs, which started amazingly early at 7:30 in the morning and didn't let out until two in the afternoon. To attend one of these weekly events was to surrender ourselves totally to a cool darkness and flickering shadows broken by a broad beam of dusty light. Such programs were concocted to fill the theaters at a time when no one but kids would go and served to relieve parents of their brood for nearly an entire day. You never, ever saw a grown-up at one of these Saturday sessions, rarely any girls, and it was the closest thing to a summer day camp we had in the Bronx.

Our parents dropped us off at 7:15 amidst a moving mass of other children still smelling of sleep from the age of three on up to about eighteen. The kids were pressed up against the wide bronze doors and they were banging their fists on the panels, as if there were a run on a bank. The front of the theater was engulfed in what looked like acres of children creating a squall of pushing and shoving until the two main doors opened inward and the crowd surged forward, cheering at breaking through the Imperial Gates of Rome in search of loot and people to torture.

It took close to a half-hour for everyone to get their tickets, because half the kids used deceits and stories intended to get the fat lady cashier to let them in half-price or free, even though the price of admission was only seventy-five cents for the whole day. Some kids would pretend to be crippled. Even blind-- "Lady, let'em in half price, he's only gonna *go* to the movie, he ain't gonna watch it." Little kids hid under their brothers' overcoats and shuffled secretly through the ticket taker's line.

By then, the candy counter was already three-deep in screaming children.

Everyone had their favorite candy, which they ate only at the movies-- Nonpareils, Jujyfruits, Pom Poms, York Peppermint Patties, Nestle's Crunch, Bit-o-Honey, Sugar Daddys, Sugar Babies, Junior Mints, Good 'n Plenty, Payday, Charms, Chuckles, Milk Duds, Baby Ruth, Clark Bars, Mounds, Starbar, Walnettos, Tootsie Rolls, Turkish Taffy, M&Ms, and Peanut Chews. Bon Bons were a big seller, except no one ever figured out how to eat those intensely cold, chocolate-covered morsels which were too large to fit whole into a child's mouth and too sloppy to eat in bites. The aroma of fresh popcorn carried throughout the theater, into the loge and up to the balcony. For many of us, it was breakfast.

By the time everybody was in their seats-- not necessarily sitting on them, but near them-- a new chant went up, demanding the start of the show. Whistles, shrieks, and the notorious Bronx cheers we claimed to be experts at rang out, until slowly the theater began to darken, and the chanting stopped as a roar of excitement erupted at the sputtering sound of the soundtrack running through the projector. The tiny square window of the booth suddenly shot out a cone of light that cut through the darkness and a picture of Bugs Bunny rippled atop the heavy curtains being drawn apart as the beloved Looney Tunes theme came up. There were yelps of joy, with kids screaming at each other, punching each other in the arm, throwing popcorn in the air, knowing that this was to be the first of at least ten cartoons that would serve as a prologue to the main events of the day.

The cartoons rolled, one upon another, without let-up-- Bugs Bunny, Daffy Duck, Donald Duck, Chip 'n Dale, Tom and Jerry, Popeye-- one would end, the next would begin, for over an hour. We enjoyed the titles and screen credits almost as much as the cartoons, and we would cheer animators like Ub Iwerks and voice magicians like Mel Blanc.

When the cartoon segment ended, it was followed by an episode of a twelve-part serial whose cheap production values were evident to even the youngest among us. The cheesiness of these heavy-handed, black-and-white thrillers made by studios with names like Mascot, Grand National, Republic and Monogram was numbingly bad. We fully appreciated the awfulness of the acting, the predictability of the plot, the usage of footage from other serials we'd already seen, and the consistent deceptiveness of the cliffhanger endings that showed how the hero this week escaped from what was inescapable in last week's episode. No one was ever fooled by seeing the hero seeming to crash his plane into a hillside or get crushed to death by a room whose walls came in on him from every side. We knew the next episode would show him parachuting out of the plane or finding a trap door at the last minute, and the only real suspense was in wondering if the director could make the escape even vaguely believable.

The serials had names like "Panther Girl of the Congo," "Don Winslow of the Navy," "Tim Tyler's Luck" and "Gene Autry and the Phantom Empire." The authors of these serials had an uncanny and seemingly boundless knack for working the word "doom" into the episode titles-- "The Dungeon of Doom," "The Flight of Doom," "The Pit of Doom," "The Mineshaft of Doom," and so on, and the heroes were given fearless names like Crash, Buck, Duke, Jack and Dick and all wore leather jackets and baggy pants. Their sidekicks had names like Fuzzy, Buzzy, Buddy, Timmy and Jimmy. Their girlfriends all wore jodhpurs. The villains, who appeared to be of Eurasian blood, wore black hoods, robes, and floppy ear coverings so stupid looking that we could never look at a picture of a member of the Ku Klux Klan without remarking how much he looked like the mad scientist in "Crash Craddock Versus the Cobra." The villains were unremittingly evil, had no use for women, and, despite an evil genius that allowed them to control world events from a truck trailer, had a dismal record of hiring complete idiots to help them in their plans to dominate the universe.

These were the last years of the movie serials, which were already becoming fodder for Saturday morning TV, and Hollywood's major studios had pushed special effects far beyond anything the serial makers could hope to mount. By the age of seven or eight, we already regarded the serials as artifacts of our childhood, even though we still acted out their hokey plots at home and called each other names like Buzz and The Dragon.

By the time the serial ended, it was ten or ten-thirty, and at least a third of the audience was lined up outside the rest rooms. This was when they showed the coming attractions, which always contained upcoming adult movies with names like "With a Song in My Heart" and "Roman Holiday" none of us would ever want to see. It was amazing to us that the trailer writers and editors could make just about any movie look and sound like the most exciting thing ever made. They'd use the word "NEVER" in every possible context: *"NEVER HAS A LOVE BEEN SHOWN WITH SUCH PASSION!" "NEVER HAS THE SCREEN DARED TO TELL SUCH A TALE IN ALL ITS UNVARNISHED TRUTH!" "NEVER HAS GENE TIERNEY LOOKED MORE RAVISHING!"* So we'd throw in our own lines, like *"NEVER HAS RICHARD EGAN HAD SUCH BIG PECS!"*

Next came a western with a title like "The Man Behind the Gun," "The Stranger Wore a Gun," or "Thunder Over the Plains," all of which Randolph Scott starred in 1953. Audie Murphy made four westerns that year, including two-- "Gunsmoke" and "Ride Clear of Diablo"-- that opened the same day. The other big western stars of the era were Gene Autry, Roy Rogers, Kirby Grant, Wayne Morris, Rex Allen, Dale Robertson, Keith Larsen, and Guy Madison.

We had our favorites and indulged in endless debates

over who could outdraw whom in a gunfight or who could beat the crap out of another in a bar room brawl. We were thoroughly acquainted with these actors' mannerisms, drawls, hats, horses and guns, and, depending on the studio that produced them, we knew the exact sound their fists made as they socked a guy in the jaw and the precise whine of their bullets as they ricocheted off a rock.

After the western came a break. The lights went up, kids squinted and yelled, "Shut 'em off!" and a silly little man who looked like a toad with a toupee on came out on stage to harangue us for all sorts of supposed evil-doings. He'd be greeted with derision, paper cups were tossed onstage at him, and paper clips whizzed past his head.

"Right, *right*! Keep it up and there'll be no main feature," he'd scream. "You boys better quiet down now or we'll end this show right now. I'm not kidding"-- a piece of gum flew past his head and stuck to the screen. "Right, *right*, that does it!" Then he'd get up on his toes, cup his hands and yell toward the rear wall, "Mr. Projectionist! *Mr. Projectionist!* I do not want the next movie shown until we have absolute silence in this theater. Do you hear me, Mr. Projectionist?"

He must have, because he dimmed the lights for a moment, then turned them way up. A shiver went through the crowd, and everyone shut their mouths.

"That's better," said the toad man on stage. "Now, if everyone remains quiet, we shall announce the winners of the raffle."

This was a nice part of the day in that it broke up the screen entertainment with a little live suspense. There would be a bicycle, a wagon, and a month's worth of movie tickets given away to three lucky kids, and Mr. Toad knew how to drag this thing out until Mr. Projectionist got all the reels in order for the main feature.

"Right, now. I will pick the first ticket stub from this

glass bowl--I hope you all saved the other half of your stub, didn't you?" There was some commotion in the audience as kids scrambled to find their stubs, and there were a few comments about stealing in the crowd.

Mr. Toad straightened his ugly tie and put his hand over his eyes, then reached way down, swished his chubby hand around and came up with the first ticket. "The numbers are, um. . . 3, 6, 6, 4, 0, . . . and the final number is. . . 4!"

A lone voice among a chorus of moans rang out, "*I got it! I got it!*" And before Mr. Toad had time to say, "Well, come up here, young man," the kid was halfway up the aisle. Of course it invariably happened that an older kid got the wagon and a younger kid got a bicycle he couldn't even mount for another three years.

The raffle over, Mr. Projectionist brought down the lights, and it was time for the main feature, which on this particular summer's day was in 3-D-- the brand new process that made stuff leap right out of the screen at you.

You had to wear these cheap cardboard glasses to bring the two images into focus, and you spent most of your time squinting and moving the glasses around on your nose so that your eyes would focus.

Few of us had seen a 3-D movie at the time because the first one--a low-budget piece of junk called "Bwana Devil"-- had only come out a few months before, and its amazing success goosed Hollywood studios into full-scale production of a slew of 3-D movies unleashed upon the public in the spring and summer of 1953. "House of Wax," a horror movie directed by a man blind in one eye, named Andre de Toth, debuted in April, was quickly followed by a western named "Fort Ti" a month later. "It Came from Outer Space," based on a story by Ray Bradbury, was next, and there we were to see it.

We were all terrified as the titles came up, for they came up at a slant, seeming to leap out over the audience. We sat there, adjusting the flimsy glasses on our noses. "I can't see *nothing*!" "How dya work these things?" "Is this the way it's supposed to look?"

The titles were accompanied by that eerie wee-*ooooo*-wee sound that evoked deep space and galaxies beyond the dreams of mortal men. And here it was, floating right off the screen into our laps. We'd reach up to try to touch it and grasped only air. Ten kids screamed in unison, "Put ya hand down, ya jerk!"

The trouble with 3-D movies was that while the special effects were pretty cool, the majority of the movie just looked out of focus, and after an hour or so, your head started to pound and your eyes ache. So that even though "It Came From Outer Space" had been tinted by the studio in "scientifically perfected eye-resting Full-Sepia Mono-Color," by the time Richard Carlson and Barbara Rush had roused the townspeople to the fact that aliens had actually landed in the Arizona desert, it was tough going to keep focused on the action, and you kind of wished the thing was over. Actually not all that much happened in "It Came From Outer Space," there was a lot of talking and staring into the dark sky, but it was creepy enough to keep us quiet, you got to see the aliens, and the 3-D effects really worked.

By the middle of the picture kids had resumed farting, shooting paper clips at one another, and running up and down the aisles. The candy counter had been pretty much polished off, and a lot of kids were feeling bloated and tired. Just then, as Richard Carlson discovered an alien had turned one of his friends into a zombie, we heard a voice up in the balcony. "Oh, jeez, I'm gonna puke!"

This was very bad news. Without a moment to prepare, everyone knew what was about to happen. The kid heaved forward on the railing, made a sound like a goat, then tossed up every bit of candy, popcorn, soda and ice cream he'd put away over the past six hours. It flew out over the audience in a vile-smelling spray that rained down over half a dozen rows of downstairs seats.

The crowd went crazy, half of them screaming, "Oh, *gross!*" and the other half laughing their heads off. The kids who got hit were furious and didn't know what to do, and Mr. Frog was nowhere to guide them. I thought the whole place was going to explode, but then a particularly good special effect came off the screen-- the aliens were returning to their planet-- and things settled down as the kids who got puked on headed for the rest rooms to clean up any way they could.

But the stench lingered in the air. The moment the house lights came up and we all saw the extent of the puke on the seats, we ran for the door, gagging and laughing and saying what a great movie it had been. A few other kids said they felt sick too.

We hit the door and barreled through it into the brightest sunlight we'd ever seen. Squinting painfully from the blast of light, we must have looked like a horde of five hundred Chinese kids breaking out of prison. We were worn out, full of sugar and popcorn and movie plots. My mother was sitting in the Chevy across the road, honking her horn and waving at us. We got in the car, gave her a one-word review of the day's entertainments, told about the kid who threw up, and then went home and turned on the TV.

CHICKEN.

By Rob Mariani

Walking out on to the black steel of the train bridge that hung over Pelham Bay, stepping from railroad tie to railroad tie with the murky green water 30 feet below made me feel afraid and dizzy.

But you couldn't tell a boy you had just met that morning that you were afraid, especially when he was two years older than you and had invited you out on to the bridge to show you something. I wanted Franky Lyons to like me and be my friend and show me other things that the older kids did, so I tried not to look down through the railroad ties.

Pelham Bridge, as it is called, was not in our little neighborhood, not part of the Country Club Road enclave. I was at an age now when venturing out past Bruckner Boulevard was an intriguing adventure. Franky Lyons was from up by Tremont Avenue and just the fact that he was from a different neighborhood seemed to hold out the promise of new horizons and fresh adventures. And so I'd followed him on my apple- green Shelby bike, up along Bruckner, past the Pelham Bay Park train station and on up the Shore Road towards City Island and Orchard Beach. We hid our bikes in the scrub behind the Pelham Bridge Riding Academy and struggled through the underbrush to get up onto the train bridge.

The bridge was almost a half-mile long. Trains going from New York City through the North Bronx and Westchester County and on up the coast of New England traveled this bridge. Silver streamliners full of business people and travelers; and long, slow- moving freight trains carrying goods and produce to and from rail heads all over the country.

Franky was out in the middle of the bridge now and waving for me to come ahead. There was a hot July wind blowing as the tide came back up the Bay and I tasted the salt in it.

"It's almost 3 o'clock," Franky said, looking up at the sun. "The train comes at about quarter after. When it gets to the edge of the trestle back there you gotta be ready to jump. But the *first* one to jump is chicken. OK? You have to wait as long as you can."

I nodded. I had never jumped from anything near this height and I didn't for a moment believe I could suddenly do it. As I stood there next to Franky in the hot sun looking down at the rippled water far below I felt a coldness and then a hotness on the back of my neck. My fists kept clenching and unclenching and a thin layer of perspiration broke out at the base of my spine beneath my baggy swim trunks. The steel track under my feet felt like it was burning through the soles of my shoes, and there was a glare coming off the water so that I could not see more than a few inches beneath the surface. It was quiet now except for the lapping of the water under the bridge and gulls crying overhead like babies.

"Remember," Franky was saying, "You've got to hit the water like this." He held his right hand perpendicular to his left to show the angle of entry and I noticed his fingers trembled slightly.

"How deep is it?" I asked.

"Oh, it's plenty deep enough. And wait'll you see down there. It's really something."

I felt a faint vibration under my feet.

"Hey, shit! The train's coming! It's early!" Franky said shading his eyes and peering down the tracks. I followed his gaze and saw the pinpoint of light at the place where the rails converged. Then I could see a small black shape like a fly and there was a light in the middle of it.

Franky stepped up to the narrow handrail and leaned out over the water, his arms behind him holding onto the rail. There would be no room for a person when the train was there on the tracks. There was only one way off the bridge now.

I stepped over the handrail too and hung facing outwards, holding on with my hands behind me like Franky was doing.

"Remember, the first one who jumps is a chicken."

Franky was looking over into my face to see if there was fear there and I tried to hide it by smiling back and showing my teeth but my arms were shaking and I felt sweat on my palms as they gripped the thin steel guard rail.

I looked down into the leaf-colored water and felt like I was already falling, like in an elevator when the floor goes downwards under you. Then a loud bell began to ring somewhere up in the rusting superstructure of the bridge. The warning signal that the train was on the bridge and I felt like I wanted to pee. And there was the sound of the train now too, the metal wheels grinding along on the metal rails, a rumbling, rolling cacophony that kept getting closer and bigger. The bell startled me so much that I almost lost my grip on the railing. Then I looked over at Franky, who was laughing and working his feet like a diver at the end of a diving board, getting a grip with his toes so he could push off just right. There was a red light down at the end of the bridge where the train was coming from now, too. A red light flashing on and off.

The sound of the train engine had gotten enormous and I could see the smoke pouring out of the locomotive. It was a big, lumbering freight train and now the engineer had probably seen us and was blowing his horn. It was so loud and harsh and ragged sounding that my chest began to hurt and I could feel my heart thumping inside.

A small shower of silver fish broke the surface of the water-- bait fish, shiners-- casting little shadows on the top of the greenish water. I looked over at Franky who was between me and the train that was filling the sky now with its huge bulk and its overpowering sound and when Franky released his hands from the guardrail so did I. I was so concentrated on watching Franky float through the air that I forgot to point myself at the right angle to the water the way Franky had told me to and I went down and hit the water hard with my chest and torso. There was the brain-rattling impact and the shock of the cold water all at once covering me and then a dull roaring sound in my ears as I felt myself sinking deeper into a dark, liquid universe.

I sculled with my arms, pushing against the brown-green heaviness that closed over me and then I was looking into almost pure blackness. There was a high-pitched whining in the center of my head as if a stream of bubbles was escaping through my ears.

In my confusion and with the impact of hitting the water, I had become disoriented and I propelled myself away from the surface, towards the dark bottom. It took me a moment to realize it but when I felt the pressure getting stronger and stronger around me I wheeled about and looking upward, saw the silver roof of the water above. It looked such a long way off, too far for me to ever hold what little breath I'd gathered as I'd hit the water. And the high-pitched whining continued in my head.

116

Slowly I began to rise. Clouds of bubbles billowed around me and raced to the top where I wanted to be. I stroked again and kicked with my feet and glancing down to make sure I was going in the right direction this time, I saw a huge, dark shape some distance beneath me. Its presence so startled me that I almost opened my mouth and let go of the small pocket of breath I was trying so hard to hold onto. I looked back again through the murky water and saw that the shape was oblong and the size of a small building. I realized that what I was looking at was a gigantic freight car resting upright on the muddy bottom, its sliding doors flung wide open to reveal even greater darkness inside. The boxcar was covered with rust and barnacles and it had turned the same color as the water but I could still see a few traces of white lettering on the sides. "Virginia..... Produce....." Something else illegible.

I floated up over the roof of the hulking mass, my lungs hammering now against my ribs and my vision starting to contract into a tunnel shape as I looked up at the silver light. My vision grew dimmer and dimmer until there was only a small point of light and just as that was about to go out my head broke the surface of the water.

There was a rush of dry, hot air against my face and I heard myself gasp. I swallowed, letting some of the sharp tasting salt water go into my nose and down my throat. It scratched and I coughed to clear it.

I looked around for Franky. Overhead I could hear the rumble of the train which was still passing over the bridge. Something made me think that Franky might have been trapped in the submerged freight car. I called his name but my voice was drowned out by the noise of the train that was still passing overhead on the black bridge, and then the train was gone and I called out again into the shadows beneath the bridge. All that I heard back was the slight echo of my own voice and the slapping of the little waves against the pilings that supported the bridge.

"Hey! Franky! Where are you! Franky!"

There was a small splash like a handful of sand falling into the water and then I thought I heard laughing. It was Franky's voice laughing, distorted by the echo under the bridge. I searched the wrinkled surface of the water. Finally I saw Franky clinging to a rusty steel ladder that ended about two feet above the water line. In a few strokes I was to the foot of the ladder looking up at him.

"Did you *see* it under there? Did you goddamn *see* it, Robby?" Franky said breathlessly.

"Yeah," I said spitting water out of my mouth and thinking about the big shape of the boxcar underneath my feet. "It scared the hell out of me. You should have told me it was there." Franky tried to laugh but water went into his mouth and he coughed instead.

"I wish I coulda seen it when it fell off the bridge," said Franky.

I reached up to the bottom rung of the ladder and realized I didn't have the strength left to pull myself up out of the water. I slipped and went under and for a moment I was back among the green, slow motion shadows and looking down at my feet they seemed white and unreal like a dead person's. Farther down below my feet I thought I saw just a hint of the boxcar's roof and it seemed like it was moving up towards me.

I came back up and saw Franky's laughing face. His teeth looked very bright in the shady darkness of the bridge. Franky had climbed up onto a small rusty platform on one of the bridge's steel girders and he pulled me up until I was able to climb the ladder myself. I worried that Franky might feel my arms trembling.

We climbed to the top of the trestle and sat down to rest on the edge of the tracks, our feet hanging over and our chests and sides still heaving.

The friendship was not a day old yet and I found myself staring off down the tracks and wondering what could be coming next and how much better it could possibly be.

NEW VOICES.

By Rob Mariani

Suddenly there were new voices in our house at 3305 Campbell Drive. Men's voices talking in hushed tones behind their hands into each other's cocked ears. Occasionally one voice would rise against another.

"*Will* you answer the question? Why won't you simply *answer*? Are you now, or have you ever been a member of the Communist Party? Yes or no?"

The response was low, mechanical. "Senator, I refuse to answer on the grounds that it might tend to incriminate me." Deadpan. Monotone.

Then a crowd of voices, murmuring and punctuated by the sharp banging of a wooden gavel. The voices subside and the low-talking goes on with much clearing of throats and tense, inexplicable pauses. Holes torn in a sound track.

Rarely a woman's voice would break the low bass notes. Tired and sad. "Senator, I'm trying my best to help out here...."

Accusations. Innuendoes. Indignation. Fear. Hour after hour of it.

In the early fifties, these New Voices crept into our house and suddenly everyone seemed nervous. The gray, faceless men who ran our country in Washington, D.C. were surfacing right here in our living room on the flickering black and white TV set that had been designed to look like a piece of furniture, but which had overnight turned into anything but. Now it seemed like an arm of the government, reaching right there into the room with you.

They were called "The Army-McCarthy Hearings," conducted by "The House Un-American Activities Committee." There weren't a lot of army uniforms in evidence, as I recall. There was one heavy-set man in a dark suit, his hair slicked back, a dark 5 o'clock shadow over his jaw. He leaned into his microphone. He huffed and puffed. His voice sounded ravaged, smoky. He was daring people to deny that they were Communists. "Commies." "Reds." "Pinkos." "Fellow Travelers." The lexicon of names proliferated as the hearing progressed. The man in the dark suit "suggested" that the people he questioned were liars and spies, trying to overthrow our government. Supplant it with Russia's.

Why, I wondered in my 10-year old mind, would anyone want to do such a thing? Nothing was better than America. We'd won the War. We had big cars and boats and restaurants and houses with backyards and golf courses, and movie stars and... *cowboys,* for God sake. Pretty soon there would be helicopters parked in our driveways just as *Popular Science* Magazine had predicted. And cars that turned into speedboats.

We had TELEVISION!

Where could there possibly be any room for improvement here? Who would want to overthrow any system that gave us all this?

We'd seen the European people in the newspapers and in the movie newsreels. The Russians were not light-hearted and gay like the Americans. They all wore heavy overcoats and fur hats and it was always winter there, and their language was hard on the mouth. Their cities looked dark and old and crumbling. If that was Communism, who would want to exchange Democracy for it? Who'd be crazy enough to not want what we had here?

Ironically, it was television that brought these disturbing voices into our home. Not just the disembodied voices anymore, as with radio. Now there were faces, too. Men the color of shadows, their heads almost life-size, just inches from our own faces. They pointed their hairy fingers at each other, hid behind their hands as they whispered to each other.

Another man, McCarthy's consort, his Tonto, with hooded eyes and a large eagle-like nose kept his face emotion-less. His voice inaudible. He whispered clandestinely into McCarthy's big hairy ear, the two men brushing jaws, covering the microphone to keep us from hearing things we should not hear.

The new faces and new voices began to take over. Every day when we came home from school they were in our darkened living room like some winter weather front. Tense, extraordinarily tense, their faces so close up you saw their pores, their pimples. They took over the airwaves so that we, the children, could not watch our newly-beloved TV shows. "Action in The Afternoon." "Howdy Doody Time." Cowboy movies with Tex Ritter and Fuzzy St. John. "Lucky Pup" with Phoodini and Pinhead. And "Time for Beany."

They were all being pre-empted, crowded off our screens by these arch men. It changed our carefree afternoons into uncomfortable, confusing head-achy hours of endless adult conversation that went around and around and back on itself.

They changed us. They changed our parents. And we did not even realize it. Gradually, the hushed tones took over our lives and it seemed we began to speak that way ourselves. Our father, drawn into the drama of the hearings unwillingly at first, soon became fascinated with who was being questioned next, who was on the spot. Sipping his martini, he shook his head in disbelief at how deep the corruption seemed to have gone. He got on board with it at first, wanting McCarthy to clean up our government. Get rid of the Commies.

Soon though it became enough just to be brought before the Committee. If you were there, you must be guilty. Must be doing something "un-American." Nothing you could say would change that now.

People from high places, movie stars, former heroes, tumbled into the unstoppable process and were chewed up, tainted, destroyed. They were coerced into "giving up" their friends. Betrayal to save your own hide was rampant. This Committee's hunt for un-Americans became as inescapable as the concept of Original Sin. And it all *had* to be true, it *had* to be valid... because there it was, ON TELEVISION! Live from our Nation's Capital.

What we saw was the process but not the results. But instinctively, I began to hate the men who were asking the questions. Not just because they had preempted our TV programs, but because they were cruel and ruthless. They oppressed people and bullied them and all I wanted was for these hearings to stop clouding up our TV screen.

It would in retrospect be referred to as Television's "Golden Age." But the medium that brought us all those great shows also brought us their oppressors. Many of the creators of the best early TV programs were victims of the McCarthy hearings, as I learned much later in life.

But TV was so resilient, so many-faceted, and so ruthlessly revealing and relentlessly bright, that it wore itself out like a comet, and exposed even those new voices of intolerance that sought to dominate it. TV won. They had lost.

UNCLE RED.

By Rob Mariani

As I said before, we grew up surrounded by uncles and by men that we called uncle. They were all part of a constantly expanding picture from which we drew our understanding and definition of what it meant to be a man.

But when I think of the term "uncle," the person who comes most immediately to mind is my Uncle Red. He'd married my mother's sister, Corinne, the beauty of the family.

Red was as handsome as Cosie was gorgeous. His real name was Tom but they called him Red because of his hair. It wasn't really red, but more a kind of a chestnut color. Still, I thought it was wonderful that someone could actually be named after a color. For a while I searched in vain for other color names I might adopt for myself, but somehow "Browny" was just a bit too canine and "Blackie" sounded like the name of some movie bad guy.

Uncle Red was about six-foot-two, which by our family's standards was close to a giant. When I first met him at the end of World War II, he was still wearing his U.S. Marine Corps. uniform and I thought he was some kind of movie star because he was so good looking. A kind of combination of Cary Grant, John Wayne, and William Holden.

One of my earliest memories of Uncle Red was seeing him drive up to our house on Campbell Drive in his huge black Packard limo. Built in the 1930's to be driven by a chauffeur, the car had a spacious back seat with luxurious fold-down couches, a sliding glass panel that separated the driver from the passengers, and bud vases. *Bud Vases*, for God sake! The car's engine alone was the size of a locomotive and as the Packard rolled down the sleepy, narrow streets of the Country Club neighborhood like a chrome-trimmed leviathan, it definitely turned heads.

"Yeah, that's my Uncle Red's car," I'd say proudly as my friends and I gawked at it cruising by.

Although I was just a little kid at the time, I instinctively understood from the expression on Uncle Red's face when he got behind the wheel, the sheer exuberance that driving a car like this could engender. I recognized that this was one of the exalted privileges of being a grown-up. On hot Saturday afternoons Uncle Red would take us for rides up to Pelham Bay Park. Sometimes we'd park and get out and just prance around the green, open fields, tossing a soft ball or a football.

One time Uncle Red brought a wooden boomerang with him that he acquired in the South Pacific. I watched in amazement as he flung it way out across the field and saw it come arcing back in a huge circle. I thought he could do just about anything. Of course when I tried to throw the boomerang, it pitched directly into the sod about four feet in front of me and stuck there.

Afterwards, Uncle Red bought us chocolate-covered Good Humor bars from the Good Humor truck and as the creamy sweetness melted on my tongue I stuck my head out the window of the Packard and inhaled the wind blowing against my face.

When Red and his wife, Cosie, had a son they named him Sean. He was the first little baby I'd ever had a chance to relate to. I'd play little hand games with him through the bars of his crib and help wheel him in his stroller.

When Sean was about a year old, he came down with one of those illnesses that kids seemed to come down with at that age—an unexplained high fever. Even though my father was only a chiropodist, everyone in the family regarded him as "practically a doctor," and so they often came to him with medical problems first, before gong to a real doctor.

One humid Sunday morning after Mass, as the family loafed around reading the papers, we heard the unmistakable sound of Uncle Red's Packard pull up and stop in front of the house. Uncle Red came bursting through the door. He was wearing khakis and a sleeveless undershirt that exposed his fair white, freckled Irish skin and his brawny Marine arm muscles. His face looked gray, his blue eyes wild and frightened.

"Al. Sean." He said grimly.

Red and Cozy were living at Grandma Sofia's house just two blocks down from us on Campbell Drive. Suddenly it seems, baby Sean had started to go into convulsions.

Without asking what was wrong, my dad leaped up from the kitchen table and he and Red were out the door. I heard the Packard's wheels screech even before I heard the sound of the car door slam shut. I ran to the kitchen window. Campbell Drive is a fairly narrow street and Uncle Red's Packard was much too long to make a U-turn on it, and so he simply slammed the car into reverse and barreled backwards down the three blocks to grandma's house, his arm looped over the back of his seat.

As I learned afterwards, when Red and dad got there, Sean was turning blue and Cosie was frantically saying her rosary and pleading with St. Anthony to save her child. Even though my dad was only a foot doctor, he'd had enough medical training to know what to do. He grabbed the baby and filled the bathtub with cold water, then plunged the quaking, blue-skinned infant into it. It did the trick and a few minutes later, Sean's temperature was back down to a safe level, the crisis averted. Thinking back on this dramatic incident, what I remember most vividly is the look on Uncle Red's face as he came through our doorway and uttered his terse, two word appeal for help. Scared. Concerned. Grave. But also somehow confident--sure that he had come to the right place for help and that his brother-in-law, Al, would of course save his son's life. That was the kind of communal feeling you had in that small, protected little "village" we called a neighborhood. The support system was always there and for the most part, it worked.

As we grew up, Uncle Red and Aunt Cosie moved away to the woods of Connecticut where they raised five sons and a daughter. Red worked in Manhattan for a company that sold pre-recorded, closed-circuit TV programs to hotels. The summer before my senior year in high school, Uncle Red got me a part-time messenger job at his office in the spectacular new glass architectural wonder called The Seagram Building on Park Avenue. Even more impressive than the soaring architecture to a teenage boy in the midst of puberty, however, was the fact that Uncle Red had not one, but *two* gorgeous secretaries—one blonde and one brunette, just like Betty and Veronica of Archie Andrews' comic strip fame. I'd walk around the office after they'd left the room just inhaling their perfume and marveling at how they moved around in their high heels, the petticoats swishing. It seemed to me exactly how girls were supposed to smell and move.

That same summer when I was seventeen and starting to become interested in jazz, Uncle Red and my dad took me to Birdland, the original, self-proclaimed "jazz corner of the world."

My father met Uncle Red and me after work, and we had dinner over on the West Side at a little place called

Vesuvio's. There were black and white blow-ups of the eponymous volcano on the walls and the manicotti was melt-in-your-mouth-sensational.

After dinner we hopped in a cab and made it over to Broadway and 52nd Street. At the top of the stairs, Uncle Red paid the admission fee for us to a sweet-smelling black girl with luxurious eyelashes who seemed to float like a tropical fish behind the big round glass ticket window. We descended the two flights of stairs into the dark, smoky nightclub and Uncle Red deftly tipped Pee Wee Marquette, the infamously rude and diminutive maître de/emcee. Pee Wee showed us to a table that was right next to the piano at the foot of the bandstand. Best seat in the house.

As we took our seats, "The Amazing Bud Powell" was at the piano with his trio. He laughed to himself and sang along to his incredible be bop lines like some kind of be-witched little demon. My dad and Uncle Red exchanged raised eyebrows, Powell's quirky behavior re-enforcing every junky stereotype they both had about jazz musicians.

I was totally absorbed by the music and to this day I can hear the notes Bud Powell played and the sound of the bass and the drums in that intimate, dark atmosphere that defined for the world what a jazz club was.

When the Basie Band came out, the power of their col-lective playing practically lifted me off my chair. This was the year that Basie's famous "April In Paris" had become such a big popular hit. Unusual for a jazz instrumental.

"Big Joe" Williams was singing with the band. I was still much too new to jazz to understand what was really going on here, but I knew instinctively that I never wanted to hear music played any other way again.

With a single wave of his right index finger, Basie was able to levitate the trumpet section from their seats in the back row where they produced that miraculous sound full of joy and spontaneity.

What I saw and heard that night changed the way I listened to music forever. And like so many pivotal moments in one's life, this one for me, will forever be associated with my big tall Uncle Red, the ex-Marine, master of the boomerang, un-rivaled Packard-driver, and just about everything an Uncle should be.

GARBER'S.

By John Mariani

It would be impossible to overestimate the importance of the corner candy store to anyone who grew up in New York in the 1950s. At its most basic level it was a place to buy just about anything you couldn't get at the grocery, all stuffed into racks and drawers and closets, so that you merely had to ask for a tin protractor, a box of staples, a Mother's Day card, a model airplane, lip balm, paper cups, a loose-leaf binder, Sen-Sen, eyeglass cushion-ers, a Spaldine, a map of the United States, an Erskine Caldwell novel, party hats, a pair of socks, an ant farm, the new *Action Comics*, a black comb, Halloween masks, chalk, magnets, and an assortment of gag items including stink bombs, hot pepper chewing gum and fake dog dirt, and the owner would reach over and pull it right out of some corner.

All good candy stores were alike in the same ways, and their familiarity, their unchangeable atmosphere, their noise, and their specific smell-- a mix of tobacco, candy, newspaper and human being smells--were as imbedded in our consciousness and as ritualized as going to Mass. In many ways the candy store evoked the same feelings of security, melodrama and hopefulness. Its appeal was in always knowing it would be exactly the same as when you left it the day before and in not knowing what would greet you on your return.

The slightest alteration was unsettling. You'd go in one day and find the magazines had been re-arranged in the rack or the pretzels moved from one end of the counter to the other. We hated change like that, as much as if the priest at Mass had suddenly come in with a new haircut. Yet you always had the feeling that when you barreled through the door one afternoon, you'd see or hear something amazing, like the time a grown man showed up wearing shorts and black socks as if this was Florida, or the time a kid's mother came in to tell her son his father'd been crushed to death under a construction crane. She didn't tell him that, she just stood at the door and called calmly to him as he spun around on the counter stool, "You'd better finish your soda and come along. Your father got sick at work."

Our candy store was called Garber's and it was on Middletown Road. It was, of course, set on a corner, just as they all were, and we assumed that all candy stores were owned by one Puerto Rican cigar company or another because there was always a Te-Amo or Garcia sign above the door. Two brothers named Garber owned the little store. They were German Jews who had bought the store back in the forties from another German Jew and didn't do much to change anything except to put up a bright new 1951 Breyer's Ice Cream sign over the mirrored wall behind the marble counter.

The two men were always there, no matter what time you dropped in, from early in the morning when they brought in the morning newspapers through the day, when the afternoon papers arrived, and on into the night, when people came by for cigarettes, ice cream and magazines and men stopped in to ask for directions to the Parkway Motel under the El.

The Garber brothers always dressed the same: White,

short-sleeved shirts, black trousers and black sleeveless sweaters, and they always had the same dour look on their face. For two guys who spent an awful lot of time attending to children, they seemed to hate kids, always telling them not to touch this, get away from that, and threatening to call your mother if you got out of line.

The two men were almost indistinguishable, except for one important thing: One of them had only three fingers on one hand and no thumb on the other. No one ever knew how he'd lost them, but we conjured up all sorts of grisly scenarios. I just assumed they'd been blown off playing with fireworks, just like two of my own grandfather's fingers had been. One kid said Mr. Garber'd been born that way, and another said it was from some disease he'd picked up in the tropics and they had to cut the fingers off with a rusted penknife and no anesthesia. But none of us could believe Garber had ever spent any time anywhere but the candy store, so we discounted that one. There were theories that had to do with a bucket of acid and mobsters who wanted to muscle in on the store's dismal profits and a real good one about how he'd burned them off vainly trying to save his infant daughter from a fire in their house, although Garber never mentioned being married or having kids. Maybe the wife was burned to a crisp too. We'd come up with a new theory about every three weeks or so, but no one ever had the courage to ask him what had happened. He wouldn't have told us anyhow. He'd just say it was none of our goddamned business.

Whatever happened, it was impossible to keep your eyes off those gnarled, smooth stumps as Garber mixed an ice cream soda for you or scooped up some penny candy in his hand. It was pretty awful to watch him do that, but we drank the sodas and ate the candy anyway and no one ever got sick as far as we knew.

For all its typicality, Garber's might well be packed up and sent to the Smithsonian as a perfect example of the architecture and lay-out of a post-war urban candy store, from the worn marble counter and spinning stools to the inlaid wood of the cabinets and soda fountain and the black and white tiles of the floor. Garber's was very small-- maybe fifteen feet long and ten feet wide--and, if you got more than five people in there, it started to get crowded. If it got too tight and someone looked like they were about to start something, Mr. Garber would wave his stumpy hand and say, "Take it outside or don't ever come in here again." That was a powerful threat, because not being allowed into Garber's was like losing one's link to the neighborhood. You didn't have to earn a place at that counter but you didn't want to be thrown out of it either. There was simply too much to do and see at Garber's.

Just inside the door were the magazine and newspaper racks. The newspapers came in bales-- there were at least ten on the counter every day, from the *Bronx Home News* and *Journal-American* to the *Irish Echo* and *Il Progresso*. There were horserace journals, sports papers, and used car listings. All of them cost a nickel or less, and if you had a dime or a quarter, you'd probably take your change in penny candy or gum.

The magazines were arranged in a careful, ascending order so that the comics were within reach of even the smallest child, and the ladies' magazines like *Ladies Home Journal, Good Housekeeping* and *Woman's Day* were to the right.

Then, in some kind of incomprehensible order, were the general interest magazines like *Saturday Evening Post, Collier's, Look*, and the new *TV Guide*.

And above them, out of harm's way, were arranged all the men's magazines-- an astonishing array of sex, violence and terror of such irresistible temptation as to taunt anyone over the age of seven. It almost seemed that the Garbers had spent hours setting the covers so that the top edge of *Argosy* just barely covered the middle of *Police Stories* at the exact point where a ravishing redhead's exposed cleavage would have revealed parts of her anatomy we could only dream about. There were so many men's magazines, each with a cover so graphic in its depiction of unspeakable torture, rape and mutilation that you'd think about it for days after you first saw it, and you watched from the counter when an adult took one down from the rack and started flipping through it and you caught a glimpse of the insides. If the covers were so intensely horrific, how much more grisly and enticing could the gritty, black-and-white insides possibly be?

The cover of one war magazine showed an American G.I. strapped to a chair, his face bloodied, with a chiaroscuro light worthy of Caravaggio thrown onto his muscular American frame. In the foreground stood a tall, muscular blonde, seen only from behind, dressed in tight-as-sin Nazi leather, a whip dangling from her right hand as her other hand began to clench with rage. The cover line for the story, printed in thick slanted red letters, went, "WHEN THE GESTAPO COULDN'T BREAK ME. . . THEY BROUGHT IN ILSA!" Another war magazine showed a G.I. in torn uniform, tied hands and feet with wire to four stakes in the ground. The wires cut into his wrists and ankles, which he had to hold up at a certain angle because if he let them drop. . . THE WIRES PULLED THE PINS ON FOUR HAND GRENADES! There were some cackling Jap soldiers in the background, though I wondered why they'd stand so near to a guy who was tied to hand grenades.

The crime magazines were so overtly sensual that they made your stomach churn. They depicted only two kinds of women-- very buxom, not-so-innocent girls about to suffer the most heinous of all indignities, and completely wicked, equally buxom sirens forcing good men into committing criminal acts. What kind of fabrics were these women's clothes made of so that they looked like a second skin? This was not the kind of cotton or wool worn by any woman we'd ever seen, not even in movies with Jane Russell or Veronica Lake. What could it possibly feel like to have such a girl pressed up against you? Would you faint?

There was never all that much blood on those covers, but it was right near the surface, just under those black negligees and nylon stockings, and you could smell the smoking guns and perfume coming off the girl's hair as surely as you could smell the sweetness of the candy and the aroma of burnt coffee behind the counter.

Mr. Garber was protective about his customers' morals, an experienced and shrewd judge of character. He knew the older boys bought some of those magazines to show to the little kids, who would come back into the store with their eyes bugged out and their mouths taut. But as long as the little kids were in his store, he'd stop them from even so much as riffling the pages of such seamy magazines. "Hey, *HEY!* Get avay from der dirty books. I tell you vunce, I tell yuh mudder der next time. You just keep avay from dat kind of filth." None of which he had problems selling to anyone who looked like he was over the age of eighteen, whom Garber would always ask, "You vant a paper bag for dese?"

The little kids had to content themselves with the comics and make do with ogling the no-less-shapely figures of Betty and Veronica in the Archie comics, which invariably had at least a couple of panels of those perfect teen queens in their underwear or bathing suits.

If you could take your eyes off the magazine rack, you'd also find a display of greeting cards, every one hopelessly sentimental and geared to an upcoming holiday. They were all in pastels, usually with flowers on the front, and inside about a dozen lines of doggerel no one ever had the stomach to read through.

Above the cards were paperback books, many by Mickey Spillane, most of which had covers similar to those of the men's magazines. Some were popular bestsellers, like *The Caine Mutiny*, *Battle Cry* and *The Blackboard Jungle*, and many had a little cartoon figure of a kangaroo on their spine.

Above the books was a shelf of toys and games, which

Garber's carried for those parents whose children suddenly announced they had to get a gift for a birthday party the next day. Garber's didn't sell many toys, except when the water pistol season rolled around in April. Then there was a run on the new models in clear colored plastic that gave the water in them a distinctive taste that was as good as any bottled soda on a hot day.

In the corner of the store was a phone booth, with a folding door that didn't close and wasn't about to be fixed any time soon. The olive drab interior was clean but countless numbers and heart symbols were written or scratched into the wall. Garber's would take messages for people in the neighborhood who didn't have phones, although many times the messages would get written on a paper napkin and absent-mindedly slipped under a soda glass and forgotten. Which is how many a kid got a good smacking for returning home an hour after their mothers had told Mr. Garber they had to be home.

Next to the phone booth was a cabinet with sliding glass panels behind which was the stationery, school tablets, loose-leaf and other writing supplies. Pink erasers, midnight blue ink bottles, yellow pencils, red notebooks, and black-and-white marble composition books. Nothing smelled better than these last items, and when you opened them and jammed your nose into the sewn crease, it was the cleanest smell in the world. You'd run your hand over paper lined in aqua-blue ink, and carefully fill in your name and address and grade and teacher's name and subject. You could start fresh with a new composition book.

At the beginning of each year you'd also get to buy brown paper covers for your new books. They had a picture on the front of a policeman holding up his hand to remind you to cross the street carefully.

Next to that was the small, glass display case full of penny candy. The packaged candy was up from next to the cash register, with the cigarettes and the gum. Behind this case was the really good stuff, the local sweets that you bought in handfuls and bags. There were chocolates, nonpareils, jellybeans, mints, pecan clusters, marshmallow bananas, and hard candy. There were tiny chocolate figures we had taken to calling "colored babies" after the priests told us that calling them "nigger babies" was a venial sin. There were long strips of paper stuck with colored sugar dots. The trick was to get them off the paper without the paper sticking to them and coming off on your tongue. And there were also little pie-shaped tins-- no bigger than two inches across-- filled with a kind of icing and accompanied by a tiny tin spoon. They were so sweet your teeth would ache.

You certainly couldn't have such candies everyday, not because they were expensive but because they were simply special, and so you had to earn candy like that or wait till a certain day of the week to get it.

Stretching half the length of Garber's was the main attraction-- the soda fountain counter, which was always smooth and cold to the touch, so in summer you'd spread your hands back and forth across it pretending to be indecisive about what you were going to order. Like most candy stores, Garber's cooked no food-- that took place in luncheonettes, which were considerably fancier spots-- so that you were left to decide between a hard pretzel stick displayed in a cylindrical jar or a soft pretzel, which was stacked onto a wooden stick.

Both went well with whatever you ordered to drink. Ice cream was hand-packed. They'd slip a stiff paper carton into a metal sleeve, and started jamming ice cream into it, forcing it down with the edge of a the scooper, making sure it was packed tight. The consistency of the ice cream was perfect by the time you got it home, soft at the top, pliable at the middle, and absolutely delicious on the tongue.

A "black-and-white" was what we called a chocolate soda with a scoop of vanilla ice cream. Malteds were made with milk, ice cream and malt powder in a noisy blender whose whine was not unlike the dentist's drill, and they'd pour you a glass three-quarters full and slap the frosted metal canister on the counter next to you for seconds.

A wonderfully ornate, very old Coca-Cola bottle opener was affixed to the wall behind the counter, but it was never put to use opening Cokes. Cokes and other sodas were made from scratch by the two owners, who would squirt a thick syrup from a silver spigot into a glass, add some crushed ice, set the glass under the seltzer spigot, jerk down the lever and run the seltzer into the syrup and ice till it was mixed just enough so that some of the syrup sank to the bottom and added a sweet underpinning to the drink.

Then there was the egg cream-- the mother's milk of New York-- a simple mixture of Fox's U-bet chocolate syrup (made in Brooklyn), a little milk and seltzer. No egg, no cream. In fact, the name "egg cream" itself implied that the simplicity of the recipe in no way indicated the kind of finesse and refinement it took to make one. A good soda jerk had to know the precise amount of chocolate syrup-- added with soft, measured squirts-- to give the drink ballast and richness. Then in went an inch or so of milk chilled so cold so as to contain tiny ice crystals. The mix was swirled with a spoon. Then the glass was set under the seltzer spigot at a 37-degree angle. Then came the finesse part: The seltzer would be added in a wide stream, incorporating a certain amount of carbonation into the chocolate milk. When the liquid reached a certain level and foaminess, the spigot would be adjusted to a strong, thin jet, which, when mixed vigorously, mounted into a creamy topping that looked exactly like whipped egg white. The bottom of the glass was then wiped with a cloth and it was set before you-- glistening, fizzing, with two inches of "cream" on the top and slicks of chocolate inside the glass.

Egg creams were drunk in two ways: Either knocked back like a shot of whiskey or sipped-- none too daintily-- so that there was time for some of the chocolate to drop to the bottom of the glass, which gave a final kick to the pleasure of it all. There were those who argued vociferously of behalf of one drinking technique or the other, and, depending upon the candy store you went to, you could get into a big argument whether a glass or a paper cone cup was preferable for making egg creams. Straws were optional, though for most purists, they turned the whole pleasure of drinking an egg cream into an infantile exercise.

The best thing to do was to get your egg cream in front of you, take a big slug, lick off the foam from your lips, take a bite of pretzel, then swivel around on the stool and hope to catch a glimpse of some guy taking down a copy of *True Detective* from the rack.

THE DOCTOR'S DAUGHTER.

By Rob Mariani

Every day, it seemed, more beautiful things came to him. And what amazed him was that there always seemed to be plenty of money to pay for them, to say yes to owning them. More than enough.

Only a few years out of medical school and already Dr. Perrotta's practice was more successful and lucrative than he had ever dreamed possible.

He bought himself the best house on Campbell Drive diagonally across the street from our much more modest 4-family home. The Doctor bought the house the same day he saw it. It was three-stories high, made of brick with a Spanish tile roof built to resemble a Mediterranean villa. It occupied a prime lot right on Pelham Bay looking across at City Island and southward at the graceful, silvery span of the Whitestone Bridge. One of the things Dr. Perrotta liked most about the house was the half-acre backyard with its small plot of grass and its concrete seawall with steps going down to the beach. Immediately upon moving in, he began filling the vacant spaces in the yard with an eclectic collection of statuary, birdbaths, fountains, religious icons and marble urns. Things he'd seen in picture books about Italy. He even had a miniature version of the Fountain of Trevi installed, along with flagstone paths. There was no real plan to the backyard display. It was completely random. Neighborhood people driving by would crane their necks to catch a glimpse of the young doctor's handiwork.

He had a gazebo built and planted grape vines to tangle around it. On summer nights he and his wife and three daughters would dine there by lantern light, tended by their Spanish house-keeper, Maria, and their gardener/butler, Charles, who donned a crisp white jacket for the occasion.

The interior of the house bore equally eloquent testimony to the doctor's extraordinary good fortune. A full-sized indoor swimming pool, the kind usually associated with motion picture stars in the 1950's, graced the rear of the house. In winter the Perrottas could swim in the warm aquamarine water looking out through the glass walls at the gray, wintry Bay. Cherubs, naiads and cupids adorned every corner of the pool area and the water fed into the pool through the mouth of a carved stone lion.

For our struggling middle class family living just across Campbell Drive from the doctor, it was like dwelling on the outskirts of a castle where we were sometimes granted tantalizing glimpses of the royal inner sanctums.

Two or three times a year, huge new cars would appear in the Perrotta driveway. Usually they were Cadillacs with chrome bumpers and sexy tail fins like Japanese goldfish, or sometimes Chrysler touring cars with long aircraft carrier— size hoods, plush gold upholstery and Landau roofs.

One early summer day we heard a strange burbling sound coming from the water behind the doctor's estate. Straining to see around the corner of the house, we caught sight of a long, sleek mahogany speedboat with red leather seat cushions and a swept-back windshield. At the helm sat Dr. Perrotta wearing a jaunty white admiral's cap and brandishing a long, dark Cuban cigar. He gunned the deep baritone inboard engine and the lacquered hull rose alertly up out of the water like a startled egret and sped off down Pelham Bay leaving behind a tail of spray.

Soon, the young doctor began to feel he needed to protect his domain as it proliferated, and so he acquired a pair of watchdogs. Like everything else he possessed, they were the biggest and most expensive available. Two Great Danes—a rare all-black male he named Dux, and a tawny tiger-striped female name Sheeba. Dux stood a menacing four feet high at the shoulder and his mate was almost as large. The doctor was not a tall man and when either of the dogs stood on their hind legs and braced their front feet on his shoulders, they towered over him. He soon realized that walking them in tandem on a leash, or even one at a time, was a physical impossibility. The dogs were too strong and willful and they'd pull him all over the sidewalk and into the street. And so he sent them both off to "college." In the Bronx, at that time, this was considered just slightly less extravagant than sending a daughter to medical school.

Dr. Perrotta's embarrassment of riches was not confined to inanimate things. While still in medical school, he had married a beautiful, raven-haired Italian aristocrat named Gilda. In their first two years of their marriage, she had presented him with two lovely daughters named Dolly and Dolores. The girls were just 7 and 8 when a third little girl, Dorrinda, was born. Dolly and Dolores were gorgeous in the breathtakingly dramatic way that movie stars are. They had haloes of dark, curly hair, enormous flashing brown eyes, long, luxurious eyelashes, and the most perfect white teeth that 1950's orthodonture could provide when cost was no object.

But it was little Dorrinda who from the moment she was born enslaved the doctor. Her olive skin and heart-melting smile never failed to ignite feelings of indescribable love in the doctor's heart. The entire family doted on baby Dorrinda but the doctor worshipped her. Miniature playgrounds, swing sets, a real pony, a child-size racing car with battery powered motor—whatever he thought might amuse or delight her, he found and laid at her feet. He even hired another maid so that Maria could devote her full attention to baby Dorrinda.

One day, in the gray, predawn light of late September, the doctor and his wife were awakened by a strange rumbling sound at the back of the house as Hurricane Carol swept up the East Coast and into the mouth of Pelham Bay. The storm was in their backyard hurling 25-foot waves against their seawall. As the tide reached its peak, the storm reached full ferocity.

Looking out of their glass solarium, the doctor and his wife felt the entire house shudder as the waves washed up over his prized possessions. They watched in disbelief as the doctor's beautiful speedboat was torn from its mooring and smashed against the seawall. Wreckage from other docks and seaside structures was thrown like straw into their backyard. A block of water-logged wood weighing nearly a ton was deposited in the center of the Fountain of Trevi. Huge pilings and wooden planks became water-borne projectiles that bent and decapitated statues and knocked them from their pedestals.

Dux and Sheeba, the two college-graduate dogs, retreated to the top of their custom-built kennel, cowering and frightened out of their wits.

The doctor ran to his baby daughter's room and snatched her up in his arms, ready to move her to higher ground. The family gathered on the third floor and watched in silence as the storm crashed through the windows surrounding the indoor pool beneath them. The water from the pool flowed out over the backyard and became one with the roiling Bay.

Then, just as it seemed that Hurricane Carol was about to bring the Perrotta's entire house down around them, the winds and the waves began to subside and the water retreat-

143

ed.

The next morning, surveying the havoc the storm had wreaked, the doctor was surprised by the randomness of the damage. Steel pipes, two or three inches thick had been bent like straws, iron girders were twisted and snapped, while a delicate 75-watt light bulb or spindly grape vine remained in tact.

The doctor saw that his prized statue garden was a shambles and that he would have to have it bulldozed into the Bay like so much garbage. But he was not depressed. He was almost excited by the prospect of re-doing it all. It would be an opportunity to correct some previous mistakes and oversights. And he and his family were all safe.

Poking around in the rubble, he reached down to touch the shattered head of a Roman god. A slight movement next to his hand caught his eye. At first he thought it might be a snake but looking closer, he saw that it was the sickly gray, hairless tail of a rat.

The violence of the storm had forced hordes of water rats out of their holes and up into the rubble. Now they were all searching for new places to colonize and the nearest structure was the doctor's house. He envisioned them pouring into the walls and beneath the floors of his cherished house, working their way into the plumbing and finally into the rooms where his children slept.

In minutes he had an exterminator on the phone and the very next day a team of men appeared with traps and poisons.

When Dr. Perrotta arrived at the Emergency Room, many of the people that knew him and worked with him looked away as he ran down the hall past them. He was too intent on reading the numbers on the doors to notice. He was searching for room 234 where they'd told him his youngest daughter, Dorinda, was. When he finally found, it, he burst in. Gilda and his two older daughters and the maid Maria were all there, tears streaming down their cheeks.

His wife stood up and tried to put her hands on his chest, but he brushed her aside and moved right to the bed where Dorinda lay, wan and lifeless on the white hospital sheets. They had already removed the tube from her throat, the tube which had failed to suck all the rat poison out of the child's system.

Dr. Perrotta was not a doctor now. He only knew that the procedures they had performed on Dorinda had failed. *How*, he demanded to know, *how could such an appalling thing have happened?*

The maid, Maria, was shaking her head and crying, no, no, no. She did not want it to be her fault. She had looked away for a moment. Just left the room for a few seconds. But that had been long enough for little Dorinda, playing around on the floor, to pick up the rat poison which had been laid out disguised as a blob of red jelly. The poison that had been meant for the rats had gone straight into her system. In seconds her throat closed and she passed out, never regaining consciousness.

Back at the doctor's house on Pelham Bay where the water had become all quiet and sparkling again, the rats were dying too. You could see their bodies floating in the tide, their mean little mouths frozen in a sneer. But many survived the traps and the poisons and they moved into the hollow places under the doctor's seawall, and into the cracks left in the foundation of the house. The dogs caught a few but there were too many. And at night in the doctor's bedroom between his wife's deep sobs, he could hear them inside the walls, trying their claws against the plaster. Soon the rats were moving up the cement driveway in the dark and across Campbell Drive and into the neighborhood.

145

JUST ONE DAY.

By John Mariani

Kindergarten was not a sure thing for a child back in the '50s. Some kids went, some didn't. My brother had but for some reason or another it didn't seem a priority for my parents to send me. Then, all of a sudden, in the middle of a semester, it did.

At first my mother just broached the subject with me, hoping I'd *want* to go. "There's lots of other children there, and you pretty much just play all day," she said, tousling my brown hair. But I had not the slightest desire to go to kindergarten, especially a public school kindergarten blocks and blocks from my house, across the Bruckner Expressway. I was perfectly content to stay home and, with the suspicions all children have of parental urgings, I felt kindergarten had nothing to offer me and probably would make me miserable.

When the urging didn't work, my mother switched to a kind of benevolent push, indicating she and my father had "already talked about it," which signaled to me they'd made the decision to send me. I grew panicky. "No, I don't *wanna* go, I *won't* go! I *won't*!" I screamed.

My mother caressed me. "Darling, go for just one day.

Just one single day. And if you don't like it, we won't make you go back."

At five years old, I hadn't yet had enough experience with my parents' promises to tell whether this one would hold. "I *hate* kindergarten," I blurted out, pretty sure I was going to lose the battle.

"Well, go for just one day. Who knows, you may love it."

Yes, I had lost the battle.

The next day, dressed in a fresh shirt, corduroy pants and a sweater with reindeer on it, I was dropped off at P.S. 12 by my mother, who was allowed to bring me straight to the classroom as I choked back tears. In those days there was no discussion of "separation anxieties." My mother hugged me and gave me a kiss on the cheek and said, "You'll have a great time. I can't wait to hear all about it when you get home." Then she left for what seemed to me the first time in our lives.

Because we had had to check into the principal's office before going to class, I was fifteen minutes late. Added to this was the fact that the semester was already half over and I was that wretched thing, "the new kid." The teacher was a middle-aged woman with black hair and glasses and a sweater that looked as if she wore it every day.

She took me by the hand and led me into the classroom, which smelled like children. It was large, with big windows and high ceilings, so that every squeal had a slight echo to it.

The room was littered with toys—blocks, little cars and metal trucks, dolls and puzzles. There was a blackboard with writing on it I could not understand, and, since it was approaching Thanksgiving, the walls were hung with cardboard pictures of Pilgrims, Indians, and turkeys. There were about twelve children there, each quieting down and turning to look at me.

The teacher brought me to the center of the room and said, "Children, we have a new little boy joining our school today. His name is John—" (she turned to me and whispered, "Your last name is—I hope I get this right—Mar-ee-annie?")—"John Mar-ee-annie, and I want you to make him feel welcome." She then pointed to each of the children and ticked off their names.

With that she let go of my hand and said, "Now you go have fun and make friends."

I stood motionless for a moment as all the children turned back to what they were doing, not acknowledging me in the least. And then I saw what a moment before I was too scared to notice. One of the boys had the horrible, horrible face of a monster. A face whose features were pulled taut, the skin a sallow gray color streaked with brown, and barely any hair on his head. His eyes were weasel-like, eyes I had seen in nightmares and in comic books.

I felt terrified and couldn't stop staring at him, though he'd turned back to playing with his toy truck. The teacher saw that I was unable to move, my eyes wide with fear. She crouched down before me, looked me in the eyes very seriously, and said, "That's Peter, and he had a very bad accident. He was burned in a fire, and that's why he looks like that. But he's a very nice boy, and you'll get used to the way he looks very quickly."

I could not imagine becoming used to the face of a monster, even one only five years old. He was small as the horrible troll under the bridge in the Billy Goat Gruff story. He had the eerie smile of the Cheshire Cat in "Alice in Wonderland." Even his hands and fingers looked like a zombie from "Tales from the Crypt."

I wanted to run, screaming after my mother, who was long gone. But I couldn't utter a sound. Then, a little girl came over to me and asked, "Do you want to play with me?" I noticed nothing about her except that she was a normal-looking child with bright eyes and all her hair. I nodded, and she took me to a corner of the room where she was playing with blocks she had stacked into a column. But I was still stricken by the boy with the burned face and I couldn't play.

As the morning wore on, my fears had barely subsided, and a half-hearted attempt at putting together a simple wooden puzzle was left undone because a piece was missing. But the morning seemed to go fast, and by 11:30 a bell rang and our teacher told us to get our coats and hats and to line up for dismissal. She had to help the boy with the burned face on with his coat. I lined up last so I didn't have to be near him, though I noticed that none of the other children seemed in the least concerned about touching him or talking to him.

We were dismissed to our parents, and my mother was there, smiling. "So how did it go?"

"Bad. I hated it."

"But why? They all seemed like such nice children."

"Mommy," I started to cry, "There was a boy there with a burned face. He was a monster! I won't go back. I hate kinnergarden!"

My mother embraced me and said, "All right, we'll talk about it later. How about we go to Garber's for an egg cream."

Despite the appeal of that notion and despite the beneficial effect of the egg cream on my anxieties, I still could not get the boy's face out of my mind. When we arrived home, I started to cry again, and, without mentioning the boy, tried to think of every other way I could to keep me out of school the next day. "The kids were mean to me. No one would play with me. The toys are all broken. And the teacher hates me. You said I only had to go for one day and then I didn't have to go if I hated it. You promised."

My mother said nothing, but later I overheard her speak-

149

ing with my father in a tone that suggested it would be cruel to send me back to such a terrifying, ill-run school with such nasty children. That night while tucking me in she whispered, "Darling, I don't want you to go back to school if it's that horrible for you. I guess you can wait till next year to start first grade."

"I won't go back to that school," I said, starting to cry again.

"No, you won't go to public school. Daddy and I have discussed it. You'll go to Iona Grammar School with your brother. Now go to sleep."

I felt relieved by my mother's words, having achieved a small triumph by making her keep her word. And first grade seemed so far away. But I also felt I'd disappointed my mother and father, and that feeling would linger. But it was crowded out that night and many others to follow by the image of the boy with the burned face.

FLOWERS OF THE RAREST.

By John Mariani

The year passed quickly and I did go to first grade at Iona Grammar School, which was a ten-minute drive away in New Rochelle. My father would drive us in the morning, and my mother would pick us up.

The school itself was a converted large wooden house in New Rochelle, with a big front porch and fire escapes on each side. There were eight classrooms for eight grades. In the first grade were 13 chairs and desks that year, and I felt privileged and happy to occupy one.

Unlike my brother Robbie, who seemed constantly to find new ways to antagonize his teachers and impress his classmates, I never had any problems at school, whose faculty consisted entirely of Irish Christian Brothers, a teaching order of young men who chose not to enter the full priesthood. Why was never satisfactorily explained. We were told that being a brother was a special vocation, a holy irresistible choice guided by God. They could not administer the sacraments or say Mass. Basically, as most people regarded them, they were male nuns. Unkinder observers would whisper that they were just not smart enough to become priests.

In high school these Irish Christian Brothers fostered a mean-spirited, guilt-driven, sexually charged version of the Catholic faith, one in which it was almost impossible to keep out of sin. In high school corporal punishment was not only condoned but sanctioned, and even in grammar school a Brother would occasionally take a ruler to a child's backside. More frequently they only threatened to use it.

But none of that was of any concern in first grade, which was to me, sheer bliss. I loved learning anything and everything. I sucked up the alphabet, arithmetic, religion, and the stories read to us and the stories we learned to read ourselves, straight out of the wonderful "Dick and Jane" primers then widely used in American elementary schools. In some universal way all children seemed to identify very closely with the colored drawings of Dick and Jane and Baby Sally on every page of the first primers. They were very much like we were, and their lives were very much like ours were. They had no great adventures, as did comic book characters; they were loved by their parents and scolded when they did wrong; they played in sand boxes and jumped in piles of autumn leaves; they had broken toys and got presents and had birthday parties. We all wanted them to be our friends, and the title of the first volume in the series was *Friends and Neighbors.*

I loved my teacher, a young Irish-American brother named Tracy, red-faced, black Irish, shiny hair, strong eyes and short stature. Never having had a teacher before, I had none to rank him against, but we always heard from kids in other classes that their teachers were horrible or stupid or mean. Many kids said they wished they had Brother Tracy.

I felt Brother Tracy had a special interest in me, because one day, with permission of my parents, he took me over to Iona College, which was on the same premises as Iona Grammar School, to be "examined" by a college professor in front of a class of college students taking a child psychology class. I was chosen because I had apparently shown remarkable aptitude in first grade (there was even some talk of skipping me ahead to second grade), and so they sat me at the teacher's desk while an Irish Christian Brother asked me questions and gave me arithmetic problems to figure out and some spatial relationship problems with cut-out figures. I was vaguely aware of why I was there and proud of whatever it was I was doing. In any case, I was back in my classroom with Brother Tracey before lunch.

In first grade the Catholic religion was revealed to us in the ways the gospels were revealed to early Christians, by wonderful stories from the bible, with an emphasis on the goodness and kindess of Jesus, who grew up a simple carpenter's son and later died for our sins. Yet there seemed just as much emphasis on Jesus' mother Mary, which was part of a traditional Irish-Catholic devotion to a maternal figure who so often held the families together.

Mary was ever forgiving. Indeed, she was the "intercessor" to her son, who apparently had so many things to deal with in heaven that the problems and prayers of little Catholic children could only get a hearing if relayed through Mary, because Jesus could refuse his mother nothing. We learned a big word, "vouchsafe," which meant Mary would act on our behalf.

We therefore learned the "Lord's Prayer," which we called the "Our Father" and the "Hail, Mary," which were prayers said repeatedly while reciting the rosary—forty Hail Marys, one on each bead, fingering the beads with our small fingers, trying hard to concentrate on every word spoken by the Angel Gabriel telling the young virgin Mary she would give birth to a child—"blessed is the fruit of thy womb, Jesus"—because she was special and "full of grace." Gabriel minced no words: the ending of the prayer, which took on a lyrical chanting in the first part, became grave. "Holy Mary, Mother of God, pray for us sinners, now and at the hour of our death." And then a closing "Amen."

None of us six-year-olds thought of ourselves as irredeemable sinners, so sometimes we would have to try hard to come up with some. Lying to our parents. Lying to our teacher. Lying to the principal. That was about it for venial sins. Mortal sins, which were very serious, grievous transgressions against God, included murder, denying Jesus, and eating meat on Friday, any one of which would send you straight to Hell if you died in a state of mortal sin. Which none of us worried much about.

The devotion to Mary was strongest after Easter, and May was the month of Mary. So, for a week or two in April, we would practice a song to Mary that we would sing to her statue on the First of May, which that year of our first grade, bloomed fresh and sunny and warm.

Bro. Tracy said we'd been practicing our Mary song and were now ready to sing it for her, or at least for her statue, which was set on a slight little mound outside our classroom. Around it were crocuses and violets, a few tulips, and some greenery.

The statue itself was typical, its iconography bound by age-old tradition. Mary was fair-skinned, with blue eyes and golden-brown hair. She wore a sky blue blue cloak and a white dress, on whose bodice was a bas-relief heart that seemed to glow with fervor. Her arms were spread at her sides, their palms seeming so white and soft, beckoning, her eyes downcast but with a faint smile on her face. And beneath her foot, a green snake with a red forked tongue was being crushed to death as it lay writhing atop the world.

Mary, herself assumed into heaven in the Assumption to join the son she'd raised, then watched be whipped, crowned with thorns, and crucified, the son she'd held in her arms when pulled down from the cross, the image of countless pietas, lived after him and then rose into heaven, as pure as the day she was born, "full of grace."

We assembled around the little rise in the earth and Bro. Tracy planted himself in front of us like a conductor. "All, right, boys," he said quietly, and raised his hands. We began so sing, very softly, some of us in another key from the other.

"Bring flowers of the rarest, bring flowers of the fairest,

From garden, and valley, and hillside, and dale.

Our poor hearts are swelling, our glad voices telling,

The name of the loveliest rose of the May."

Then, the sing-song of the verse led to a sweet refrain.

"Oh, Mary, we crown thee with blossoms today,

Queen of the angels, Queen of the May.

Oh, Mary, we crown thee with blossoms today,

Queen of the angels, queen of the May."

Our voices rose and fell on the third line, so that we climbed high up the scale before singing the slow last line, whose only high note was on the second "of," which Bro. Tracy told us to sustain until he dropped his hands.

We finished the refrain and stood in silence, not really knowing what to do next. "Now say a prayer to the Virgin Mary," said Bro. Tracy. "Tell her whatever you want. Ask her to look over you. And if you do, she will. She will always be with you, wherever you are."

A slight breeze blew among the trees and rustled their new green leaves, and the tulips wavered too. I felt as pure and white and holy as I could imagine ever being, almost on the verge of tears but inexpressibly happy.

So, as we headed back to our classroom and the bell

155

rang to send us in double-file off to lunch, I sang over and over, just to myself—

"Queen of the angels. . . Queen of the May.

"Queen of the angels, . . . Queen of the May.

"Queen of the Angels . . . Queen of the May."

THE CHAMP.

By Rob Mariani

She was certainly not what I'd expected. We'd seen pictures of her in the papers, emerging from the black, oily waters, smeared with lard and wearing a white rubber bathing cap—and in the movie newsreels of her ticker tape parade down Broadway. But the Gertrude Ederly who appeared at the Country Club beach this sunny July day did not look much like a super athlete. It was hard to believe that less than 20 years ago, while still a teenager, she had been the first woman to swim the English Channel, in 14 hours and 39 minutes.

She wore a plain white terrycloth robe as she shuffled down to the water's edge. She removed the robe and laid it on a rock, revealing a simple one-piece black wool bathing suit. It was the kind you've seen countless times in old photos of Coney Island or other beaches in the 20's and 30's. In her mid-forties now, she was only about five feet tall, and her body was—well, there's no other way to put it—dumpy. The flesh on her arms was loose and pale and her shoulders were rounded and slightly stooped, her thighs dimpled and chubby. It was hard to imagine this little lady battling the treacherous currents and cruel temperatures of the English

Channel.

I remembered my father telling me how a man in a row-boat—her coach—had rowed alongside her the whole way, feeding her bits of food and encouragement as she rolled over on her back in the choppy surf. And now here she was in person, stepping gingerly at first into the calm, olive green waters of Pelham Bay—the same waters where we kids played tag and swam relay races and ducked each other mercilessly. It was about 11 AM on a weekday morning. I remember noticing a slight stir among some of the beach blanket moms as Gertrude Ederly appeared. She was the only international champ our little neighborhood had ever produced.

I watched as she waded slowly into the water up to her hips, then she fell gently forward and with her stubby, baby-like arms, struck out in a correct but unremarkable crawl towards the horizon.

From shore, it didn't appear that she was making much headway at first. She stroked slowly, creating almost no wake, breathing every five strokes. But I looked away for a moment and when I looked back, she was almost a quarter mile out into the Bay. I watched as her little bobbing white bathing cap grew smaller and smaller. Then when she had reached the shipping lane, less than a mile out, she turned right sharply and proceeded up the Bay in the direction of the Whitestone Bridge. In a few more minutes, Gertrude Ederly was out of sight.

Life on the beach went back to normal. Kids splashed each other, built and destroyed sand castles, downed peanut butter and jelly sandwiches flecked with sand, and drank Kool-Aid from paper cups. The day wore on and then at about 5pm, when blankets were being gathered up and children sorted into family groups, a small white dot ap-peared on the horizon. Soon we could see her elbows rising and falling as she stroked towards shore. As she came closer you could see that she appeared to be swimming at precisely the same deliberate pace she'd started out at nearly five hours ago. Her tempo was exactly the same—five strokes and a breath, five strokes and a breath.

As she neared shore, I remember thinking that I'd never seen anyone so at home in the water, as if it were her natural element. I caught a glimpse of her face as she looked up and measured her distance to land. Her expression was calm and collected, like someone who had just awakened from a nap.

Her feet touched bottom, she stood up, hauled the straps of her wool bathing suit up and unbuckled her bathing cap. As she walked out of the water and over to the rock where she'd left her robe, a woman about ten years younger than her came up to her and shook her hand. "My God, Gertrude, you were gone all day. Were you swimming the whole time?"

"Yeah," she said quietly, flashing a snaggle-toothed smile. "I had a nice swim."

The woman looked at her watch. "You've been gone almost five hours." Gertrude smiled and shook her mousy colored hair loose, wiped her face with the sleeve of her robe.

The woman leaned down and put her ear to Gertrude's chest, then looked up in astonishment. "You gotta hear this," she said to her friends. "Her heart. It's not even beating fast!" She said. "It's going slower than mine."

Pretty soon everyone on the beach, about 25 grown-ups and kids, were lining up to listen to the Champion's heartbeat. Each one came away amazed.

Gertrude smiled, her face very relaxed, no sign of exertion in her breathing.

"What did you expect?" she said. "It's Pelham Bay. I grew up in this water."

COWBOY HEROS OF THE GOLDEN BRONX.

By Rob Mariani

When I was seven years old my mother decided that it was time I took horseback riding lessons. Her sister Cosie had learned to ride at that age and gone on to trick riding school where she mastered the skill of circumnavigating the barrel of her horse while traveling at a full gallop.

Horseback riding lessons in the Bronx? To my mother it seemed like the most logical thing. She had always treated her sons as though they were going to grow up to be some kind of aristocrats—private schools, suits from Bonwit Teller, haircuts at Best & Co., and riding lessons. The place she chose was the same stable where her sister had taken her first lessons, the elegantly named Pelham Bridge Riding Academy. It was only a five-minute drive from our house, just up past Pelham Bay train station and over the Pelham Bridge on the Shore Road.

Unlike the other two riding stables in the area, Park Riding Academy and New Kentucky, which only used western saddles and tack, and catered to a much lower brow, roughneck crowd, Pelham Bridge taught strictly English saddle riding. The owner, Margaret "Miggs" Sorenson, was a boney, buck-toothed, Swedish lady with watery blue eyes that looked like a pair of oysters and two gray braids wound around the back of her skull like a pair of misplaced earphones. For the entire time that I rode at Pelham Bridge, which was about four or five years, I never saw Mrs. Sorrenson wearing anything but a heavy tweed hacking jacket, brown jodhpurs and low-cut jodhpur boots. Veddy British, indeed.

She had no offspring. Her horses were her children. She babied them, she pitied them. And she worked them. It was after all a seasonal business and those "poor slobs," as she called them, had to be hacked out all summer so she could afford to feed them all winter, when no one was paying three bucks an hour to ride them. There were about forty horses in the barn, mostly hacks and four or five private boarders who got roomy box stalls instead of the narrow straight stalls the working horses were in. When there was no snow or ice on the ground, the cobblestone courtyard in front of the barn had to be swept twice a day, and even in winter, every horse had to be curried and brushed and have their hooves picked out daily. No ribs ever showed on any of Mrs. S.'s Pelham Bridge horses and in summer they were all neatly clipped, trimmed, and re-shod.

Mrs. S. revered English riding and loathed everything about Western horsemanship: too much saddle, not enough bridle, too little leg contact, too much uncollected galloping, too far back on the horse's kidneys—and the *clothes!*

On the day of my first riding lesion, I felt a little intimidated when I saw them leading my horse out of the barn. She was a big rangy, black and white mare named Pinto. My teacher, Renee, was a sweet, good-natured young lady with a mop of black, curly hair and a crooked smile. She taught me to post and to keep my heels down the very first half-hour of my lesson. Not more than 10 minutes into my first ride, I was hooked. I became so enamored of horseack riding that I asked my mother to bring me again the very next day. This, in spite of the sore aching legs and back my first lesson had inevitably engendered.

"If you ride every day," Renee said, "the soreness will go away."

For the next year I rode at least once a week, rain or shine. It was only $2.50 plus $1.50 for the instructor, but at that time, this was a bit extravagant for our family. My dad only charged $3 an hour for his chiropody services, and with two sons in private school and office rent and other expenses, it was a stretch to say the least. He suggested I try to get a job at the stable and work for my rides. To my amazement, that's just what happened and suddenly I had my first job.

I'd show up at the barn a couple of days a week after school, and on Saturdays and Sundays, and they'd put me to work mucking out stalls, cleaning tack, and grooming horses. I had to stand on a hay bale to reach their heads. On the summer weekends I'd work the pony rides, holding little kids on the ponies' backs and walking them around a small ring for 25 cents a turn.

For my efforts I was allowed to exercise one of Mrs. Sorenson's horses for an hour once a week. Sometimes if the pony ring got really busy, she'd also toss me a buck or two on a Sunday afternoon. I was getting to be a pretty good rider by then and Mrs. S. always had me exercise the horses that didn't get ridden much during the week because they were too "toppy" for most of her inexperienced patrons. I got to ride some pretty interesting steeds that way, horses that constantly challenged me to improve my riding skills.

Working at the barn also placed me in a new social environment. The stable hands who worked full-time at Pelham Bridge were guys from Hunt's Point in the heart of the South Bronx-- the Bronx everyone thinks of when they think of "Da Bronx." In their early twenties, these guys were aspiring rodeo riders. That's what they did with their time off. They rode Brahma bulls and bareback horses in small town rodeos in New Jersey or Delaware. They were rough and ready young men from one of the Bronx's toughest neighborhoods. They wore snap-button cowboy shirts, high-heeled boots and sometimes, when Mrs. Sorenson wasn't around, cowboy hats. And they were all pretty good, self-taught western style riders who adjusted with remarkable agility to Mrs. S's less beefy English saddles.

After work every evening, Mrs. Sorenson would drive her workers back over the Pelham Bridge to Pelham Bay Station where they could catch the IRT down to their cramped apartments in the lower Bronx. Before they got on the train, the stable hands would usually stop for supper at Unter den Linden—a German steam-table restaurant tucked under the rusty shoulder of the Pelham Bay IRT. The restaurant specialized in hardy, workingman fare like pot roast, meatloaf, stuffed pork chops, custard pie, rice pudding and deep black, steaming mugs of coffee. Ballast food that could restore you after a 10-hour day of shoveling manure, currying uncooperative horses and hefting hay bails. Before the War, Unter den Linden had been one of many popular German beer gardens in the early 1920's. It had had an actual overhead bower of leafy "*linden*" that created a cool, shady place to quaff frothy steins of German beer. This was before the days of universal air conditioning, of course, when people stayed cool simply by staying out of the sun and drinking lots of cold liquids. But with Prohibition came the demise of the beer garden's main reason for being. The owner of the Linden, a man we knew only as Hans, with slicked back gray hair and a sly, gnome-like smile, re-grouped and transformed his beer garden into a more generic restaurant for working men. It was open pretty much around the clock catering to night shift brakemen on the IRT, bus and trolley drivers, as well as firemen, cops, garbage men and postmen, most of whom plied their trades while the rest of the Bronx slept.

One evening, after work, sitting at the table in Unter den Linden, waiting for the orders of pot roast and ham and beans to arrive, Mikey Lopez piped up. "Hey, man, you hear about Nicky Panzella over Park how he knocked a horse unconscious?"

"No freakin' way, man," Lou Longo said, taking a long drag on his Chesterfield and expelling the smoke through his nose. "Nicky's strong but no way he's gonna knock a *horse* out." Lou was a small guy but strong from doing manual labor all his life. He was a graduate of the Samuel Gompers Trade School. His dream was to get good enough at Brahma bull riding to go on the circuit full-time and quit his day job at Pelham Bridge. Even then, a good bull rider could make some pretty serious money, if he didn't get stomped on or have his face kicked in. Which of course, they always did.

"I'm not shittin' ya," said Mike-y. "Big Poncho, he told me. Said the horse--you know that big bay gelding they call Nosey?--Poncho said he kept pulling his hind foot away while Nicky was trying to shoe him and after about the tenth time, Nicky he got fed up and he clocked him one full force on the side of the freakin' head. Horse fell right fucking over, man, and Nicky he sat down on him and finished shoeing him that way."

Nicky Panzella was a bulldogging legend known around all the local riding stables for his almost superhuman upper body strength and ability to jump from a galloping horse on to a running steer and wrestle it to the ground in under 5 seconds. (The world record at the time was something like 3.5 seconds.)

"Nicky's got biceps like baseballs," Mike-y Lopez always liked to say.

Tony Lufrano sitting across the table from Mike-y, shook his massive buffalo-shaped head in wonder, always eager to believe new stories about Nicky Panzella's feats of strength.

"Nicky could do it," agreed Tony as he managed to stuff the entire heel of a loaf of pumpernickel bread into his mouth while continuing to talk. "Nicky is like a goddamn bull," he mumbled, spewing breadcrumbs across the Formica tabletop. "You ever look at his fucking arms? Fucking baseballs."

"Yeah, yeah, but he'd break his goddamn hand if he hit a horse like that," said Lou. "Horses' skulls, man, they're like rocks, like freakin' concrete."

"He *did* break his hand," said Mikey "It's all bandaged up. I seen him. He couldn't rodeo this weekend 'cause his hand's broke." Mikey sucked up some black coffee without lifting his mug from the table.

Nicky Panzella and his wife, Patty were a rodeo couple. They'd even been married on horseback one frigid night at an indoor rodeo arena in upstate New York while their horses stood patiently, breathing steam, and the band played a country and western version of "Here Comes the Bride."

Patty Panzella was the other thing that the stable hands from all the different barns envied Nicky for. She had the kind of ass that Levis had been designed for—heart-shaped and tight as a drum. She was a trick rider. Her trick-riding saddle had a flat padded seat and a pommel that looked like a unicorn's horn, and there were handles all around the cantle. That saddle was considered the ultimate cool piece of rodeo equipment by my friends and me. Even cooler than bull ropes or bareback rigs, even cooler than sawed-off saddle bronc rigs. And, because it got to have such intimate contact with Patty's spectacular ass, we all longed to *be* that saddle.

I loved hanging around with those Hunt's Point cowboys-- almost as much as I loved riding horses. The fact was, I couldn't get enough of the feel of that huge, muscular animal between my knees. For the first several months all I'd done was trot. Then, one day they put me on a nicely coupled little seal bay gelding named Bullet. Bullet went from a walk to a trot to a canter as if he were a carrousel horse. He was the Fred Astaire of horses. And sitting to his canter was like being rocked in your mother's arms, soft as butter. All you had to do was sit to it. The way Bullet placed his feet and the way that his back rolled gently beneath you, it was like a kind of spinal massage that spread all over your body. And he would do anything you asked him to do. Jump off a cliff. Run into traffic. He was one of those horses who could make almost anyone look like an experienced rider.

The Pelham Bridge barn was everything that the Park and New Kentucky barns were not. Built in the 1930's and maintained by the Bronx Parks Departments, Pelham Bridge's barn was a handsome green wooden structure with a gambrel roof, a hayloft, and a cobble stone courtyard. The aisles in the barn were solid concrete and the stalls all had wooden floors. Bedding was changed every day (one of the jobs I did when not tending the pony riders). The barn was nestled at the foot of a hill beside the old Shore Road. The back door looked out onto the muddy channel of Pelham Bay and the big black railroad bridge where I'd learned to play "Chicken" with Franky.

The tack room was a funky little space next to the big barn. It had a pot-bellied stove and a wall full of saddle racks. On freezing winter days when the ground was too icy to ride, everyone who worked at Pelham Bridge would huddle around the stove as it glowed dull orange and the wind roared outside the rickety door. In addition to Mikey and Louie and Tony, there were also the beautiful Catholic school girls from Parkchester who worked at the barn too. They gave riding lessons in exchange for free rides. There was Patty W., and Patty D., Barbara, and Babsie. They were all about four years older than I was and thought of me as a kid, which of course I was. But a kid whose hormones were beginning to say things to him about those girls in their tight-assed Levi's-- things I just didn't understand or know quite how to respond to.

One bitter cold, snowy afternoon we were all in the tack room cleaning bridles and repairing halters. As I sat across from the potbellied stove soaping a stirrup strap, I felt a gentle touch on the back of my neck. Fingers riding caressingly up my scalp. It was Patty W., the tallest, blondest, blue-eyed-ist, most gorgeous girl of the whole bunch. And there she was massaging *my* neck! The feel of Patty's hand on my skin, the deep smoky scents of burning wood and damp saddle leather mixing with her intoxicating girl aroma was something close to a sensory overload. She kept petting me like that for a good half-hour. Like I was a cat or something. And I wanted it to go on for the rest of my life.

One bright spring Saturday as the landscape was coming to life again, and people had come out to ride at Pelham Bridge, and I was feeling more confident than ever before about my riding skills, I had what I think of as my "hero's moment." There must have been 15 or 20 customers milling around in front of the barn, waiting for their group to be mounted and pushed out onto the trail. I was coming out of the barn when suddenly there was the pounding of hoofs and a stir went through the crowd. Patches, a big drafty strawberry roan gelding with a Roman nose, came galloping into the courtyard. His was rider-less, the reins trailing dangerously behind him, stirrups flapping. He'd dumped his rider, an older man who had exaggerated his riding prowess and who was now paying for it, somewhere out there on the bridle path in who knew what condition. The crowd of onlookers scattered as Patches came to a sliding halt on the cobblestones, sparks flying from his hoofs. Louie caught up the reins and tossed them back over the horse's head.

"Bobby," he commanded. "Get up on him and go and find the guy." Instead of using the mounting block, Louie gave me a quick leg up, flinging me into the saddle like a jockey headed for the starting gate. Without waiting to even pick up the stirrups, I yanked Patches around hard and pointed him back out to the bridle path. He started to balk like I knew he would and I kicked him three times hard with my heels, holding the reins straight out over his neck and he took off at a gallop. I could hear the oohs and aahhs of the impressed crowd of onlookers as I barreled by them.

"You see that little kid ride that horse?" somebody said.

"Not even any stirrups," somebody else said.

"Go get 'em, Bobby!" Louie yelled after me.

Out on the path I galloped on a straightaway for about half a mile. Then up ahead I saw the guy who'd been thrown. He was crawling around on his hands and knees in the dust.

"Hey, Mister. You OK?"

"My teef!" he said with a heavy lisp as he looked up at me for a second.

"Your teeth? *What?*"

"My teef, I wost my goddam false teef when I went off."

I dropped down off Patches' back and started patting around in the gray dust of the bridle path, helping him look for his teeth, afraid as hell that I might actually find them.

"Shit, there they are," the man said. He crawled over to the side of the path and picked up a pale pink crescent studded with luridly white false teeth. He wiped the grit off with his handkerchief and slid the teeth back into his mouth. I was too short to get back up on Patches without a leg up, and not strong enough to give the man a leg up so we trudged back on foot to the barn together, leading Patches.

When we got back to the barn, the crowd didn't applaud or anything, but I could tell that mentally, they were clapping and cheering like I was some kind of Tom Mix. It took all my self-restraint not to strut and swagger a bit as I led Patches back into the barn to un-tack him.

For a few moments I thought I knew what Nicky Panzella went around feeling like most of the time. When I came back out of the barn, people gestured towards me with their chins and nudged each other. Get a load of that kid, will ya. And I started to imagine what the talk would be like later that night after work as we all sat around at Unter den Linden eating slabs of Dutch apple pie with vanilla ice cream and drinking deep, dark cups of Hans' black coffee.

CROSSING BRUCKNER.

By Rob Mariani

There is this deal the Catholic Church calls "the Nine First Fridays," which says that if you go to Mass and receive Holy Communion on the first Friday of every month for nine weeks straight, you get a "plenary indulgence." That means all the time you would ordinarily have to serve in Purgatory before getting into Heaven was automatically eliminated, and if you were to die at any time after completing the Nine First Fridays, (nobody ever explained why it's "9"), you'd go straight to Paradise, assuming you didn't commit any more sins before you die.

To me when I was twelve, it seemed like a pretty inexpensive insurance policy.

The only trouble was getting to Our Lady of the Assumption Church for seven o'clock Mass meant crossing Bruckner Boulevard.

As I said earlier, Bruckner Boulevard wasn't just a road or a street, it was a boundary line. It was a four-lane thoroughfare that was like the 38th Parallel in Korea. It was an invisible barrier that protected our little neighborhood from the tough guys and street gangs like the Gaylords and The

Condors. For some reason that to this day I don't fully understand, the bad guys did not cross Bruckner and invade our territory around Country Club Road.

As far as I knew, our neighborhood was not protected in any special way by the police or by some beneficent overlord with political influences. But in all the 16 years I lived there, I never saw a single instance of crime or misbehavior worse than chalking someone's driveway at Halloween, or putting a bag of burning dog shit on a front stoop and then ringing the doorbell. And in both those instances, the perpetrators were us. There were never any burglaries and, except for the time Richie Swift set the Roslyn vacant lot ablaze, there were never even any real fires or other forms of vandalism. Somehow, the place was charmed.

Once or twice a week, we'd see a green and white police car cruising calmly down Campbell Drive or parked in the shade along Country Club Road. The two officers inside always looked relaxed, as if they were on break, which they probably were.

But just across Bruckner Boulevard, we were told that bad things could happen.

Still, a plenary indulgence with its promise of a direct, do-not-pass-go entry into heaven was enough motivation for me to attempt to cross that Boulevard. I thought that perhaps since I was on a holy mission, I'd be protected.

On that first First Friday morning of early summer, the traffic on Bruckner had not really begun yet. I stopped and got off my bike and waited for the light to change. A garbage truck rolled by, heading south towards the dump, out past Edison Avenue. Out in the middle of the road there was a flock of drab sparrows enjoying a small road-kill. The light changed and I crossed, then re-mounted my bike by the building where they stored Indian artifacts for the Museum of Natural History in Manhattan.

The Church of Our Lady of the Assumption was just a

few blocks further into *terra incognita*. I locked my bike to the iron fence that surrounded the church, which for some curious reason had been built below ground level like some modern day catacomb. Its roof was parallel with the ground and you descended two flights of stairs to enter the church. I got to my pew and genuflected just as the priest and his altar boy entered the altar stage left. My fellow worshippers included three very small, very bent-over old ladies all in black telling their rosary beads with their gnarled, scaly hands; and a decrepit man of indeterminate age whose clothes gave off the distinct odor of cat piss. The service droned on in beautiful, sonorous Latin. The altar boy jangled the bells for the Consecration, the priest held the host up above him, then broke it up like a graham cracker and stuffed it in his mouth. He turned to the congregation, holding the smaller host over the gold chalice. I left my seat and went up and took the Communion wafer on my tongue. I heard the gray-haired priest whispering Latin just above my bowed head. The papery white disk stuck to the roof of my mouth and tasted like cardboard. I peeled it away with my tongue and swallowed the Body and Blood of God, taking it right into myself and then waited to see if I could feel Him moving around inside me.

I'd always thought I should exude some sort of instant glow, some mystical light once I'd taken the host. But as usual, there was nothing but the dull vacant taste of my own saliva, stale from fasting, mixed with the vague pabulum taste of the wafer. I returned to my pew, made an attempt at grateful prayer and left as soon as the priest turned to the tiny congregation and said the much awaited, "*Ite missa est.*"

I was nervous about getting home now, back across Bruckner, but since it was still quite early morning, and everything in the neighborhood seemed very calm and still, I decided to make a quick stop at Garbers. I parked my bike outside and entered the store where I was immediately surrounded by sensual stimulants— the smells of chocolate candy and syrup, the overwhelming rush of images from the hundreds of comic books and girlie magazines, and toy boxes; the hum of the silver electric fan in the back of the store like the prop on some fighter plane about to take off from an aircraft carrier; and the low, grumbling sound of one of the Garber brothers' voice behind the counter talking on the phone in a heavy Yiddish accent.

Nothing could have been more opposite from the dark and holy, incense-scented church atmosphere I'd just come from.

I bought a pack of Double Bubble with the free miniature comic strip inside the wrapper. I stuffed the flat pink slab of gum into my mouth and felt the sugar rush down my throat. The cartoon was one I'd already seen about six times. As I was about to re-mount my bike, a huge long, black Cadillac rushed by me through the silent morning air. It came to a clattering halt a half block away in front of Tony DeLeo's Fruit and Vegetable store across the street. I watched as the two passenger-side doors flapped opened and three guys who were built like vending machines, wearing dark blue suits and ties and homburgs, got out. Moving with remarkable grace and speed for such big men, they ducked into the little hole-in-the-wall of a bar called The Star Tap.

The Star was one of those you-can't-see-in-the-windows places that always seemed closed except you'd see guys going in and out every once in a while.

A couple of minutes later, the three palookas emerged from the Star Tap with another man in tow. The guy was wearing a white shirt with the sleeves rolled up and he had a big white napkin still tucked in his collar beneath several flabby chins. As they were dragging him along, he started to say something but one of the guys who was ushering him out chopped him in the windpipe and the guy gagged audibly. They lifted him into the backseat of the big Caddy, banging his head against the edge of the roof once for emphasis. The door slammed shut and I saw the man's fat face, bloodied now, pressed hard against the car window. Our eyes seemed to meet across the street for a moment. There was a pleading in his gaze, a kind of silent, infantile cry in the expression on his face. The car took off up Middletwon Road and then hung a screeching left onto Crosby Avenue going towards Throgg's Neck. The only thing I knew about the area where they seemed to be going was that once you got off the main road, there were a lot of swamps.

After this brief whirlwind of activity, everything on the street seemed especially still. I blew a huge pink gum bubble, which snapped and collapsed over my nose. I sucked it in with a wet flapping noise.

In the distance I could hear the humming and grinding of the Pelham Bay Line train as it came to a stop over at the Burhe Avenue station.

And then a hand—a big hairy man's hand reached out of the open door of the Star Tap and abruptly pulled it shut. Now a few people began peeking out of store windows and around corners. Somebody must have called the cops because next thing I knew there were two squad cars in front of the Tap. One car stopped and two cops jumped out and charged through the Tap's front door. The other car turned on its siren and kept going on up Middletown Road and left onto Crosby.

It wasn't until the cops showed up that I actually started to feel maybe I should be scared. Their arrival made what I'd seen somehow officially "real," although I still wasn't sure exactly what it was that had happened. I hopped on my bike and headed back towards Bruckner Boulevard. There still wasn't much traffic and so instead of waiting for the light, I stomped on my pedals and drove across the black pavement and back down pebble-strewn Country Club Road. The moment I felt that familiar road surface beneath my bike wheels, I felt a sense of relief and safety.

My best friend, Chrissy Sheehan was coming up the street towards me on his black English racing bike.

"Hey, Rob! I was looking for you. Where were you? You go t' Mass?"

"Yeah, I'm doing the Nine First Fridays."

"Yeah, your mother said. Hey, c'mon, we're building a new fort over in back of Woo-Woof. Davey and Richie found this lumber and tar paper and stuff. C'mon."

I never made the Nine First Fridays. I fell short by exactly eight. The next month when what would have been my second First Friday rolled around, in my mind I pictured the fat man's face pressed against the car window, the strange, pleading, baby-ish look on it and I turned over in bed and went back to sleep. I heard later that the dead body of a guy, some small time hoodlum from The Star Tap, had been found in the swamp grass up around Throgg's Neck. He'd been shot twice through the head and the neck.

I punished myself mentally, accusing myself of being a faint-hearted, weak Catholic, too intimidated by a random act of violence to venture across Bruckner again, even if it meant eternal forgiveness and paradise. What I thought I'd do was wait maybe until I was an adult, maybe with a car. That way, being older, I'd have more mortal sins to have expunged anyhow.

It's not that I never crossed Bruckner. Hell, it was the only way you could get to Garber's and an egg cream. In the years to come, I would cross Bruckner Boulevard any number of times, but almost always with at least a couple of my friends.

RATS.

By John Mariani

Once in a while when our mother and father came home from dinner in New York, they'd bring us back a gift. Even if we were asleep they'd wake us up, like it was Christmas or something, and gives us these souvenirs. They couldn't help themselves. It might be one of those glass balls in which "snow" swirled around a figure of the Empire State Building. Another time it could be a collection of swizzle sticks from a nightclub like the Astor Bar.

Once, before hearing Hildegard sing at the Persian Room in the Plaza Hotel, Renee insisted Al take her across the street to F.A.O Schwarz to get us something. That night they came back, woke us up and presented us with boxes of lead soldiers made and hand-painted in England. My brother got six strutting Queen's Guards in scarlet tunics and tall beaver hats. I got a box of medieval knights painted gold, with red and white plumes and fierce war axes in their hands.

There was never any way of knowing when or if our parents would bring us home such gifts, and it was certainly not common nor a ritual to wake us out of a sound sleep. But it was clear that on occasion Renee and Al would be seized by an uncontrollable, sentimental need to see their sons awake when they got home and to watch us respond to their spontaneous largess.

One night Renee and Al came home with chocolate cigarettes packed in a clear, colored plastic box, which they'd bought at Radio City Music Hall after seeing "Singing in the Rain" and watching the Rockettes. They'd been out with the Verlins, eaten at Vesuvio's, seen the show, and driven home. They were both dead tired.

"Kids O.K?" Al asked Mrs. Brussler, the babysitter, who had been watching "The Bells of St. Mary's" on "The Late Show."

"Just fine," she said, taking the few dollars Al handed her, then adding, "They had a little disagreement right after dinner, but they were good boys after that."

Al had to drive Mrs. Brussler home to Castle Hill. When they got to her door, she fumbled with her key. "You know I never used to lock my door," she said, as the key finally clicked in the tumbler. "But I guess you can't be too careful these days."

"Guess not," said Al. "Goodnight, Mrs. Brussler. We'll see you again Thursday?"

Al drove home and left the car outside the garage because he was too tired to get out and open the garage door. He knew he'd be up early enough so that he wouldn't block the landlord from getting out in the morning.

Al went into the apartment, removed his coat and took the chocolate cigarette cases out of his pocket.

"Let's not wake up the kids," he told Renee, who was already in her nightgown.

"I'll put the cigarettes next to their beds and they'll see them in the morning."

"I don't want them eating chocolate the minute they get

up."

Al rubbed the back of his neck. "Well, you don't want them eating it at 12:30 at night either, do you? Lemme just leave them under their pillows."

"O.K.," said Renee. "I'll be in in a minute."

Al turned off the lights in the foyer and kitchen and walked to our room. The plastic Virgin Mary lamp cast a gray-gold light in the darkness, so that Al could see the sleeping silhouettes of his sons against the tiger wallpaper.

Suddenly Al screamed. "Oh my God! Oh my God! Oh Jesus!"

Renee heard him and shouted into the darkness, "Al, what's the matter?"

She flew into the room and saw her husband heading towards my bed. There, sitting squarely on my chest, was an enormous water rat, bigger than a cat, its fur black and glistening. Its eyes reflected a hideous, yellow light back at my father and its teeth were bared. I bolted up from my pillow just in time to see the thing shoot off my bed. Its claws made a grotesque scratching sound as it skidded along the linoleum into the closet.

Al slammed the door shut with such force as to shake the wall. Then I was wide awake and my father stood over me, his hands clutching my face, turning it left and right, looking for any sign that the rat had bitten or nicked me. He threw back the covers and looked at my chest, turned me over, then examined the rest of me, even though the rat had clearly not been under the covers. He picked me up in his arms, shuddering and repeating, "Are you all right? Are you sure you're all right?"

"Yeah, yeah, I'm fine," I shouted.

My father let me go. His eyes were still wide. "There was a rat on your bed. On your chest. On top of the covers." My mother was pressed against the door, almost wailing.

Rob roused himself from his bed, more fascinated than scared by the incident. "You're kidding. A rat? A real rat? Did it bite you?"

Al suddenly pushed himself off the bed and stood up. "Oh God, what if there are more in here? Renee, get the kids out of the room right away. And get me the cat."

"But what if they're in another room? What do I do if I see one? Oh, Al, what are we going to do?"

"Just take them in the bathroom. Turn the light on, look around and take them in the bathroom."

My mother did as she was told, walking out of the room into the darkness of the apartment, fearing she would be attacked by hordes of rats lurking in the living room, the foyer, the kitchen or even her own bedroom. She went to the bathroom, and, mustering all her courage, flicked on the light. There was nothing there. "Robbie, John, run in here quick. *Now!*"

Meanwhile Al had started turning the lights on throughout the house, his eyes searching every corner, looking under tables, terrified that another rat would jump from under the slipcovers. There was nothing. Then he picked up our cat, Jolo, who had been curled up on the love seat and startled by all the shouting. Al grabbed him under the front legs, raced to our bedroom, and squared himself in front of the closet door. Slowly he put his hand on the doorknob, then pulled back the door and threw the cat in.

Al put his ear to the door and listened. He heard nothing but kept listening for a full minute. There was no scratching, no animal sounds, nothing. Then the cat started mewing in what was clearly a confused and puzzled way. He began to scratch, calmly and softly, at the door. It was a soothing sound.

Slowly my father opened the door and the cat ran out. Al pulled on the closet light string and looked in. He saw nothing but the shoes piled up to the rear of the closet, which he

179

gingerly moved aside, bracing himself for the violent exit of a rat. He saw nothing at all until he glanced down next to his feet. There in the corner of the floor was a small hole, no bigger than the diameter of a baby food jar. Its edges had been eaten through, and the old wood was white and fresh where the rat's teeth had gnawed it.

Al went quickly to the kitchen and got a can of Maxwell House coffee. He took out a can opener and pushed it down into the lid of the can. The can emitted a hiss and the sweet smell of fresh coffee rose in the cold air of the apartment. He took the sharp, serrated lid off the can and got a hammer and some flat-headed nails out of a drawer. He went to the closet, knelt down, and with a deliberate fury, banged the coffee lid into place with six nails around the rim.

"What are you doing?" I asked, sitting up in bed.

"I'm keeping the goddamn rats from ever getting into this house again." He gave each nail head another bang with the hammer. "There, that should keep 'em out."

But it didn't. The next morning, when I looked into the closet, the coffee can lid had been pried open and the rim bent back away from the dark hole.

LEAVING.

By John Mariani

The rats weren't the real reason, or at least not the only reason we left Campbell Drive. We never saw another rat in the house. In fact, we might well have stayed on another year or two had the landlord, Mr. Morrison, not wanted our apartment for himself and refused to renew our lease. So we had to leave.

But the move was out of the Bronx, just as it was for hundreds of thousands of others who had grown up there and now sensed that it was not the way it had been and wasn't ever going to be again. A sea change was coming, and, reluctant as we were to leave, we felt it would sweep over us sooner or later.

There were some very specific reasons why the Bronx started to go bad as fast as it did. And much of it had to do with attempts by politicians and powerbrokers to sell the old American idea of Progress in a post-war period that was really part progressivism and part paranoia. There was an unbridled belief that the city desperately needed change and expansion, that the cramped neighborhoods had to be opened up, cleaned out, rebuilt and connected to the suburbs and to what was called the Northeast Corridor that stretched from Philadelphia and New Jersey to Massachusetts.

There were new forms of transportation, more cars on the road, more people wanting to get in and out of the cities. Traffic had become horrendous throughout New York's boroughs, yet every time a new road was built, a new highway driven through a region, or a bridge thrown across water, it solved nothing and within months served to exacerbate the congestion and traffic. Each new road became a conduit for more and more people from the Bronx, Brooklyn and Manhattan to leave the city once and for all.

A paranoia had set in. Perhaps the witch hunts of the McCarthy era fueled people's fears of impending take-over. Or maybe it was the other way around: the witch hunts and McCarthy era fed off a growing anxiety that America was no longer isolated from the problems of the rest of the world, and that everyone wanted to come here--either to feel safe or to overthrow us. There was even a suspicion that adding fluoride to municipal water systems was part of a communist plot, even though no one explained what harm could possibly come of it.

We looked around us and saw commie infiltrators everywhere. They were allying themselves with ignorant, impressionable Negroes and the tough-looking Puerto Ricans who couldn't even speak English, signing them up, getting them hooked on drugs so that they could undermine America's social fabric. And of course many of the communists were Jews. *The New York Times* was run by Jews and that was a pinko paper. So many Jews had Russian names after all, and, of course, most of the city's landlords were Jews who would do anything to make a fast buck-- even if it meant destroying their own neighborhoods.

The delicate harmony that existed among the various pre-war immigrant groups was turning to dissonance. The respect different people had for each other's neighborhoods was breaking down. You could see that in the teenage gangs, which were Italian or Irish or Jewish or Puerto Rican or whatever. But as long as you stuck to your neighborhood, everybody got along pretty well. The troubles and tensions that started to develop in the early Fifties were not so much racial as they were class struggles. And at that time the African Americans and the Puerto Ricans were at the bottom of the economic ladder, while most of the other immigrant groups had moved up into some stratum of the middle class.

You could tell just what stratum you were dealing with by walking through any neighborhood of the Bronx, from Fordham to Throgs Neck, from Mott Haven to Parkchester.

So when the neighborhoods were altered or changed by politicians and developers, the fabric of life in the city unraveled. In the name of Progress and profit-motive-- the two engines of American free enterprise that distinguished our system from communism-- long-enduring, peaceful neighborhoods were cut up and people displaced. The old ways of doing things needed to be overhauled, wealth spread around, jobs created.

The concept of "rent control" by which families lived in big, spacious apartments with only minor increases in their rent during the time they lived there kept landlords from making a fair profit from buildings that needed expensive upkeep and renovation. So they tried a new tactic to get the families out: It was called "blockbusting" and it meant that when a rent-controlled apartment finally became vacant, the landlord would deliberately move in a poor family-- meaning a Black or Puerto Rican family-- hike up the rent and then let the place go to hell in the hopes of driving out more rent-control families.

The new, indigent tenants, many of whom had their rent paid for them by the City's social services, preferred those large middle-class apartments to the old tenements of Harlem and the new tenements-- called "projects"- -thrown up by and paid for by the city.

As the poor moved in, the middle class moved out, and with a speed that was amazing to those who believed no one would ever think of leaving the Bronx. The first instance of how insidious and gangrenous the process could be came along the Grand Boulevard and Concourse in the west Bronx, which was designed in 1892 along Haussmanns's grand boulevards of Paris. This was a solidly middle class Jewish section whose streets were once lined with trees bearing the names of those local boys who'd died in World War I. After the IND subway was shoved underneath the Concourse, the trees were removed to Pelham Bay Park.

Block busting began driving the Jews out of the Grand Concourse at about the same time a far more devastating process was set in motion by New York's "master builder," Robert Moses. This was the Cross Bronx Expressway and it was conceived in 1946 by Moses-- who had quite literally been responsible for the shape, configuration and growth of New York since before the war. It was as a way of linking the George Washington Bridge and the west Bronx to the bridges he'd built across the Long Island Sound and the East River and on up to connect with the New England Thruway. The ambitious nature and complexity of this plan was bound to cause disruptions along the seven-mile stretch the expressway was to take, but the actual route Moses mapped out and rammed through, despite ardent protests from engineers and civic leaders, sealed the fate of the Bronx forever. Moses, who did not himself drive a car or even have a license, was convinced that in the Modern Age the car was king and the highways were routes into the future, even if they were outdated and jammed with traffic within months of their opening.

The Cross Bronx Expressway would be cut through 113 streets, subways, highways and neighborhoods, and go under rapid transit lines deep into the hard gneiss bedrock of the Bronx. The immensity of the plan was daunting, but its realization was devastating. The Grand Boulevard and Concourse would suffer the indignity of having three levels of traffic built under it-- a magnificent feat of engineering but a death blow to the neighborhood's integrity.

And as the Expressway moved inexorably eastward, it displaced more people, most lower middleclass Jews who lived along East Tremont, condemning old apartments in its way and along its bank, cutting people off from their parks and markets. People who had lived in East Tremont for decades were suddenly told to get out within ninety days. With the help of the Bronx Borough President and other politicians of the day, the Expressway went through just as Moses had envisioned it, and its construction took the entire decade of the 1950s, and by the time of its completion, the Bronx had been disemboweled.

After the exodus began, the Jews followed the trees that had once been planted along the Concourse to the land around Pelham Bay Park. For when Freedomland—a misplaced attempt at creating a Disneyland-style amusement park in the swamplands-- was razed, the land was developed into a housing community of astounding size and breathtaking ugliness-- 35 monolithic towers of red brick set on marshland along the New England Thruway. Sixty thousand people-- the equivalent of the population of Atlantic City at the time—moved into this monstrosity, and what had once been a theme park called "Freedomland" was now called by the Orwellian name, Co-Op City. For anyone who thought about it, the change of names pretty much summed up what had become of the Bronx by 1970.

The Italians, Germans, Irish and Scandinavians had begun to move out too. They moved to lower Westchester into towns like New Rochelle, Mount Vernon and Yonkers. When the state erected the Tappan Zee Bridge, it opened up enormous opportunities in Rockland and Orange County for middleclass whites to own their own house and land far enough away from the problems of the city yet close enough so that the plumbers, construction workers, mechanics, policemen and firemen could get to their jobs in the city in a reasonable amount of time. At least that was the intention. Eventually the Tappan Zee became so crowded at rush hours that it could take nearly an hour to get across.

By the 1970s the Bronx had become wholly symbolic of urban blight. In the south, where the gash of the Expressway ran, many neighborhoods became war zones for drug gangs that sometimes burned whole apartment buildings to the ground. That is, if a landlord had not already paid an arsonist to do it so that he could collect on the insurance. There were whole blocks that looked not unlike the newsreel footage of bombed-out German cities after the war. Such images of the Bronx became so fixed upon the public that people would shudder if they had to pass through it. A police movie entitled "Fort Apache, the Bronx" showed a city already dead, and the nickname attached itself to the borough in the way "Sin City" was attached to Las Vegas and "Murder Capital of the World" to Detroit. Tom Wolfe's novel *Bonfire of the Vanities* furthered the idea that venturing into the Bronx was to take one's life into one's hands.

For much of the Bronx there was a great deal of truth to all the bad publicity. In 1977, during Game 2 of the World Series, with the Yankees playing the Dodgers, an ABC TV helicopter covering the game hovered above the Stadium and showed a large uncontrolled fire burning not far away. Sports announcer Howard Cosell, as if to sum up the borough's death throes, told Americans watching, "There it is, ladies and gentlemen, the Bronx is burning."

And so it seemed, for as the fans at Yankee Stadium chanted "Reh-GEE! Reh-GEE!" to drive Reggie Jackson to bring the game home, the fire raged. And somewhere in the dark, burnt out streets a serial killer who took the name "Son of Sam" roamed in search of his next victim. Earlier in the summer an astonishing black-out drove the entire city into terrifying darkness, which for the poor and the desperate and the despicable meant a free-for-all for looting. At one Pontiac dealership 50 out of 55 cars on the lot were stolen that

186

night. And a priest who left his church to try to calm things down out on the steamy black streets returned to find his church looted and his altar stolen.

By then New York was officially declared bankrupt, and the rest of America seemed to see the event as God's punishment of the Sodom of the East, the Gomorrah on the Hudson. A famous New York headline quoted (erroneously) President Gerald Ford, when asked to help bail out the city, as saying, "Drop Dead!"

But by then our family was gone from the Bronx. We'd gotten out early, in 1954, when I was nine years old, just as the onslaught against the Bronx neighborhoods began. We moved up to Westchester, which, after all, the Bronx had been part of for more than 200 years. We moved into a suburb called Eastchester, on a tract of land that had months before been flat potato fields. A developer had built a score of Cape Cod-style clapboarded houses around neat, quarter-acre plots, and when we moved in on a spring day in 1954 there were no lawns, not a bush or a single tree. On the day we got there my father stuck a sprig of forsythia into the ground and it sprouted yellow flowers two weeks later, then gave off thousands of green leaves.

I had my own room, across from my brother's, on the second floor. It had eaves, and the big empty room echoed when I walked through it. I looked out over a backyard of leveled dirt, with no demarcation between our land and our neighbors'. The air no longer smelled of the ocean. It smelled of fresh soil, which the breeze carried and settled on my windowsill until the grass grew in that summer.

EPILOGUE.

By John Mariani

At the time, I didn't really mind leaving Campbell Drive as much as Rob did. He had lived there longer and the neighborhood was more ingrained in him and his friends. He was more a part of the Bronx, which had molded him, and he couldn't easily shake it off. Assured by mom and dad that he was only fifteen minutes away by car from Campbell Drive and that my father would drop him off at Mrs. Sorenson's on the way to work, he didn't put up much of a stink about leaving. In a year he'd have his learner's permit.

My parents might well have stayed on too, had it not been for that business with the lease. They might have relocated somewhere else in the Bronx, where they'd lived their entire lives, but they couldn't afford Riverdale or one of the houses along Pelham Parkway. And they had caught some of the virus of paranoia about what was happening all around us and were not immune to the charms of what much later became known as "upward mobility." Back then it was just called "moving up." It sounded like a good thing for a young foot doctor and his family to live in "affluent Westchester County"-- the adjective was stuck to the territory the way "sunny" was to Florida and "wild" was to the West. We even had a Scarsdale post office.

But we were sorry to leave. To us the neighborhood looked exactly the same as it always had. It was still neat, people still sat on the cement steps of their houses and the buses came down Campbell Drive right on time. The Sound was still gray-green and the air still smelled and tasted salty. The water still lapped on the rocks and the subway rattled off in the distance.

We were one of the first to move out, and we suffered slight feelings of betrayal, believing that if others followed us, Country Club would go the way the rest of the Bronx was headed.

In 1954 we didn't see much of the blight and the burnt out buildings that became ubiquitous in the following years. We didn't see whole neighborhoods change from the kind of middle-class vibrancy that kept them strong and secure for decades to the kind of poverty-induced despair that sucked the life out of them over the next ten years. But we knew it was coming, and we didn't want to be engulfed by it-- a not irrational fear that became epidemic in the Fifties in America.

But the remarkable thing was that our neighborhood never developed the cancer. It stayed almost completely intact, with few alterations. True, they filled in the lots where we'd played every sport in every season, and the one that led down to the Sound. They were unattractive apartment buildings but not tall enough to be a real blight and expensive enough to prevent the neighborhood from turning into Fort Apache.

The old houses stayed as they were, and generations of the same family succeeded one another. In fact, as the 1960s and 1970s turned very bad in the Bronx, the appeal and the attractiveness of our seemingly ageless neighborhood grew, and it was difficult for anyone not related to someone who already lived there ever to buy a house or rent an apartment. People told friends or relatives a house was coming on the market, and no realtor was ever needed.

As the City itself climbed its way out of numbing poverty, recessions, and neglect, so did the Bronx, which is now in better shape than it's been in decades. What was once characterized as "Fort Apache" is rapidly being redeveloped. Derelict houses are now selling for top price. The Grand Concourse is again a thriving community, its buildings' facades cleaned, its streets lined with new businesses, dry cleaners, medical offices, and flower shops.

But in all those years Country Club never really changed. It is still almost a golden little place where our memories are still part of the landscape.

And though Rob now lives in Rhode Island and I still live in Westchester, whenever he comes to visit we get in the car and drive down to the old neighborhood. Everything seems smaller, of course, not big and broad as we remember it when a walk up the block was an adventure. And the old Club itself is much the worse for wear, having been battered for decades by the Sound and having lost most of its wooden pier years ago.

So when we go back, Rob and I visit without the slightest regret that things have changed. We can still show our own kids where my lemonade stand was, where the watermelon races were held, and where the dead man in the tree hung. One time we even convinced a woman who lived in our old apartment to allow us to go inside and see where we'd slept and celebrated Christmas and ate. And the closet where the rat ran into. And the backyard where in World War II my parents had a Victory Garden.

Would we ever consider moving back there now? No, but more because we've changed than because our neighborhood did. Our lives took turns and led elsewhere, but Rob and I are inexorably tied to 3305 Campbell Drive. So when we go back the sea air smells as salty and fresh, the road still winds along the shore to the old Club, and the spirit of a wonderful era is still intact. It was a time when life moved through us, rather than our moving through life.

We can still hear the train in the distance, and if we close our eyes and listen real hard, we can still hear our mother calling us to dinner as my father's yellow '55 Chevy comes into view at the corner of Campbell Drive.

***

Made in the USA
Middletown, DE
23 June 2019